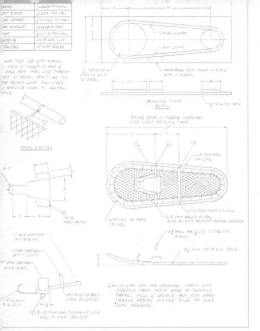

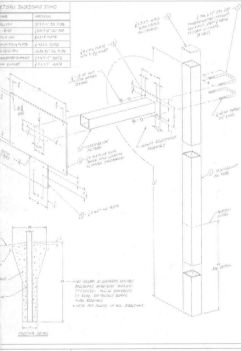

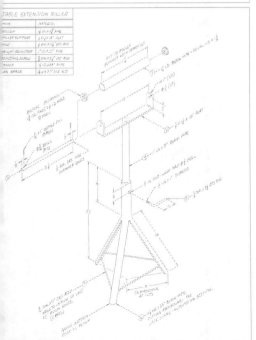

Welding Projects

James A. Ruck
Welding and Metals Instructor
Twin Lakes, Wisconsin

Publisher
Goodheart-Willcox Company, Inc.
Tinley Park, Illinois

Copyright 1999

by

The Goodheart–Willcox Company, Inc.

All rights reserved. No part of this book may be reproduced for
resale. Manufactured in the United States of America.

International Standard Book Number 1-56637-502-9

4 5 6 7 8 9 10   99   02 01

Library of Congress Cataloging in Publication Data

Ruck, James A.
  Welding projects / by James A. Ruck.

    p.   cm.
  Includes index.
  ISBN 1-56637-502-9
  1. Welding.   I. Title.
TS227.R72   1999   98-44480
671.5'2—dc21   CIP

INTRODUCTION

Thoughts on shop projects…

I grew up in the city of Chicago, completely unfamiliar with farm life. However, I got a job teaching in an agricultural community in Wisconsin. Most of my students in metalworking were from farm families. Producing equipment for their farms was a major part of our shop activities. All of the shop projects were created from necessity.

One spring there was an unusual amount of flooding in the farm fields. Ground preparation, work, and planting had to be done or the season would be a loss. Unfortunately, the standing water made this work impossible.

I had a young man in class who wanted to make a temporary field drain tile machine. This would mount to the three-point hitch attachment on the tractor. We worked on the design of the rugged device, which was to bore a four-inch diameter hole through the ground three feet below the surface. When the project was completed, I was invited to the farm to observe the first use of the "Torpedo." He had the attachment mounted on the three-point hitch of the tractor and was ready to go. I got in the cab of the huge four-wheel drive tractor, and we drove to one of the flooded areas. He backed the tractor into the water, lowered the three-point hitch, set the Torpedo into the ground, and started moving forward in low gear. The Torpedo dove into the ground as the tractor jumped and shook. I was sure that nothing could sustain such stress, but the tractor slowly moved forward. Inch by inch, the Torpedo carved a drain into the earth. Finally, we had powered our way to the low point of the field. To my amazement, I looked back and watched the pond disappear.

The water flowed through the drain that was formed by a machine produced as a shop project by a 15-year-old student. I knew at that moment what was required to make a great metalworking program.

I have found that producing projects that students like and still teaching specific knowledge and skills is what makes Technology Education classes fun and exciting. I would like to share my ideas with the many students who want to build and produce projects in school and, hopefully, bring this desire into the workplace.

James A. Ruck

CONTENTS

GENERAL NOTES FOR WELDING PROJECTS

- Read and study the drawing before starting.
- Gather all materials necessary to complete the project before beginning any individual parts.
- Before making large frame units, complete all subassemblies and individual components that are easy to store.
- Check dimensions from drawing and layout accurately. Material is expensive. Remember, measure twice and cut once. Not measure once, cut twice.
- Prepare surfaces to be welded (by machining or grinding) to develop proper weld penetrations. Refer to a comprehensive welding textbook, such as *Modern Welding* from Goodheart–Willcox Publisher.
- To ensure proper shape of the finished weldment, be sure to clamp and tack weld all joints prior to final weld. Also, preassemble any assemblies before final welding to ensure fit.
- Not all welded joints are identified on the drawing. However, where specific welds are required, the weld is identified.
- Remove all sharp or rough edges. Chamfer all corners, saw cuts, or machined areas.
- Clean all surfaces. Prime and paint with high-quality finished product. Do the extras necessary to get the desired results.
- Always weld in a well-ventilated area. Be sure to use all of the correct safety equipment, clothing, and procedures. Refer to a comprehensive welding textbook, such as *Modern Welding* from Goodheart–Willcox Publisher. Also see the *Safety* page in this book.
- Projects are produced from steel unless otherwise specified. In some cases, aluminum can be substituted to reduce weight.
- The plans are a guide to producing a project. Variations, changes, modifications, and additions are recommended to personalize the projects to your specific needs.
- Additional machines and operations may be required to produce some projects: sawing, milling, lathe-turning, sheet metal brake and shears, drilling, grinding, scroll machine.
- Where thin wall tubing is identified, electrical conduit can be substituted. However, caution should be used when welding galvanized metal.
- Project liability is up to the supervising instructor. Ensuring quality craftsmanship, correct materials, and appropriateness of project to a student's ability level must be done at the teacher-student level.

SAFETY

Dangers present in a welding shop or welding environment include heat, sparks, fumes, radiation, high-voltages, hot metal, moving vehicles, hazardous machinery, and moving overhead cranes and their loads. Using training and adequate safety equipment can control these safety hazards.

Three of the most important factors in safety on the job are:

- Staying healthy in mind and body.
- Becoming well trained in the required job or task and its possible hazards.
- Having a good attitude toward safety rules, equipment, and training on the job.

Personal Safety and Clothing

- Welders should wear appropriate clothing, such as work clothes or coveralls.
- Wear goggles or approved safety glasses.
- Wear hard hats if overhead hazards are present.
- Wear gloves, preferably with leather gauntlet-type cuffs.
- Wear steel-toed safety shoes if handling heavy objects.
- Arc welders should wear an arc welding helmet with correct specifications.

Housekeeping

- Keep floors and workbenches clean.
- Move combustibles away from areas where sparks or hot metal may fly.
- Clear aisles of tripping hazards such as hoses or cables.

Fire Hazards

- Store paint, oil, cleaning chemicals, and other combustibles in steel cabinets.
- Clearly mark fire exits, fire blankets, and extinguishers.
- Know how to use the extinguishers and blankets.
- Know where emergency exits are located.
- Know what equipment to shut down before leaving the work area.

Electrical Hazards

- Circuits or equipment carrying 220 volts or more must be well marked.
- Only competent technicians should install or repair electrical equipment.

Machinery Hazards

- Operate machinery only after thorough training in how the machine operates, its safety hazards, its safety features, correct placement of hands and feet, and the proper sequence of operation.

Fumes and Ventilation

- Dust, fumes, and metal particles are health hazards.
- Shop should normally have high ceilings for greater air volume and well-designed ventilation systems to provide adequate volume of air movement according to OSHA requirements.

Suffocation Hazards

- Well-ventilated spaces must be available when heavier-than-air or lighter-than-air gases are used in closed working areas.
- If proper ventilation is impossible, the welder must go into the space using an air-supplied respirator.

Lifting

- Learn how to safely lift objects in order to reduce injuries.
- Limits should be set on how much weight a worker may lift.

Hazardous Obstacles

- Temporary hazards should be marked by signs, fences, or barriers.
- Permanent hazards are often painted with wide yellow and black stripes.

Hand and Power Tools

- Examine hand and power tools for loose parts prior to use.
- Check power cords for frayed insulation, cuts, or exposed wires.
- Defective equipment should be returned or reported.

Designated Welding and Cutting Areas

- Safe areas for welding and cutting must include concrete floors, arc filter screens, protective drapes or curtains, and fire extinguishers. Store no combustibles nearby.

Welding on Hazardous Containers

- Never try to weld or cut a container that has held flammable or hazardous materials unless you have been trained in proper procedures.
- (See American Welding Society (AWS) Publication F4.1–94).

IMPORTANT INFORMATION

Material Identification

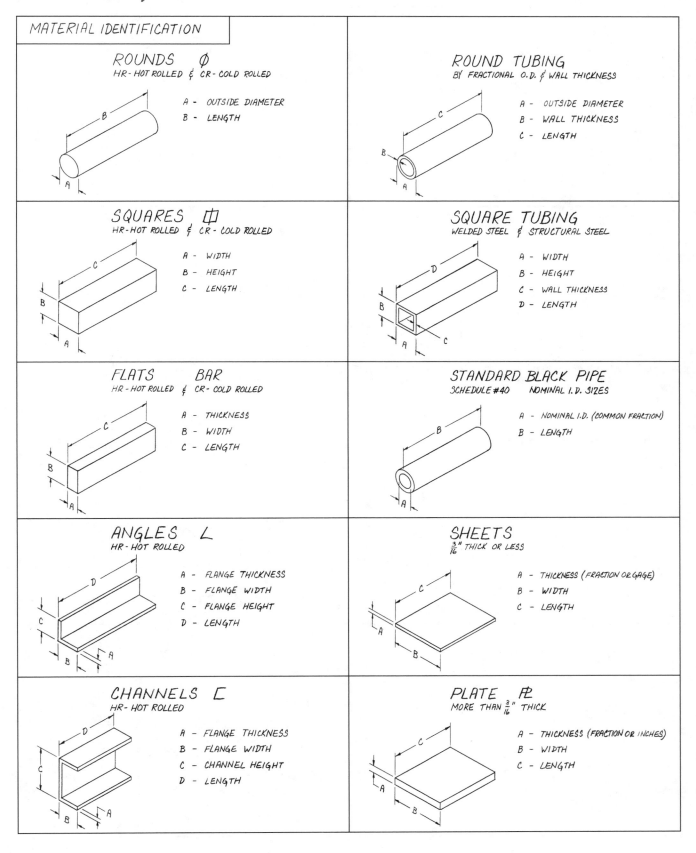

MATERIAL IDENTIFICATION

ROUNDS Ø
HR - HOT ROLLED & CR - COLD ROLLED

A - OUTSIDE DIAMETER
B - LENGTH

ROUND TUBING
BY FRACTIONAL O.D. & WALL THICKNESS

A - OUTSIDE DIAMETER
B - WALL THICKNESS
C - LENGTH

SQUARES ⊡
HR - HOT ROLLED & CR - COLD ROLLED

A - WIDTH
B - HEIGHT
C - LENGTH

SQUARE TUBING
WELDED STEEL & STRUCTURAL STEEL

A - WIDTH
B - HEIGHT
C - WALL THICKNESS
D - LENGTH

FLATS   BAR
HR - HOT ROLLED & CR - COLD ROLLED

A - THICKNESS
B - WIDTH
C - LENGTH

STANDARD BLACK PIPE
SCHEDULE #40   NOMINAL I.D. SIZES

A - NOMINAL I.D. (COMMON FRACTION)
B - LENGTH

ANGLES L
HR - HOT ROLLED

A - FLANGE THICKNESS
B - FLANGE WIDTH
C - FLANGE HEIGHT
D - LENGTH

SHEETS
$\frac{3}{16}$" THICK OR LESS

A - THICKNESS (FRACTION OR GAGE)
B - WIDTH
C - LENGTH

CHANNELS ⊏
HR - HOT ROLLED

A - FLANGE THICKNESS
B - FLANGE WIDTH
C - CHANNEL HEIGHT
D - LENGTH

PLATE ℔
MORE THAN $\frac{3}{16}$" THICK

A - THICKNESS (FRACTION OR INCHES)
B - WIDTH
C - LENGTH

Welding Symbols

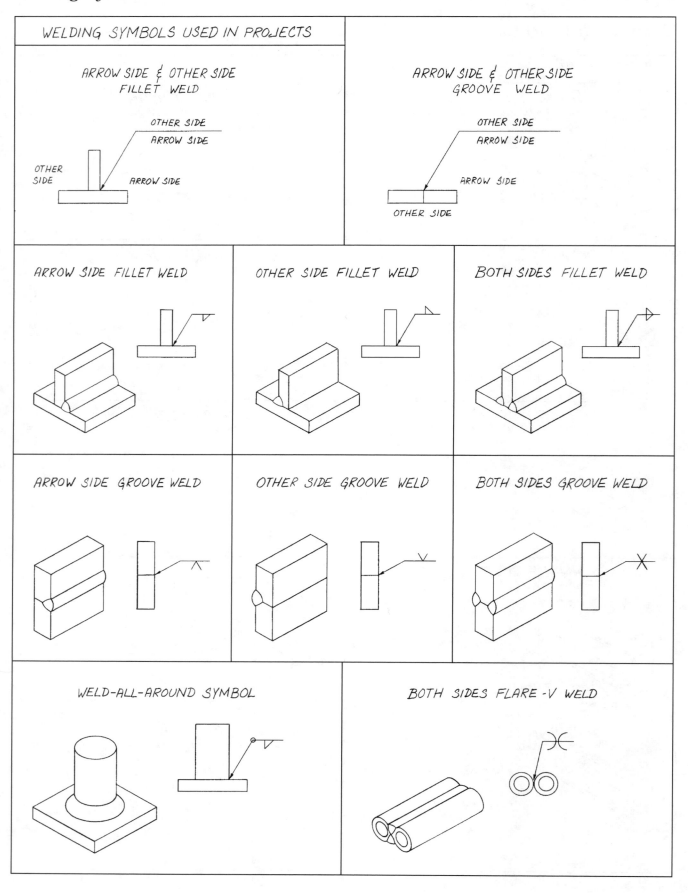

Upholstery

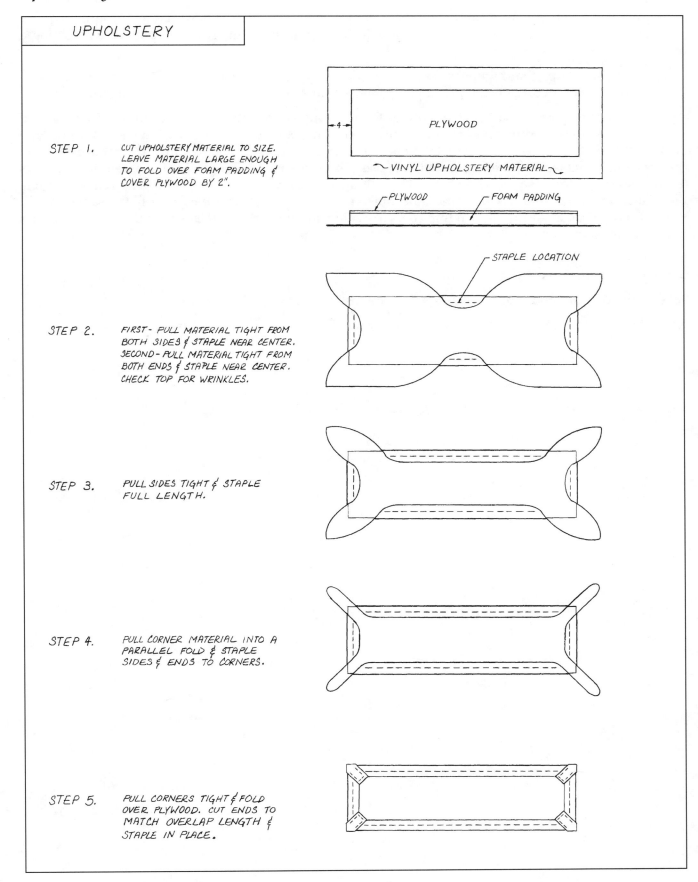

UPHOLSTERY

STEP 1. CUT UPHOLSTERY MATERIAL TO SIZE. LEAVE MATERIAL LARGE ENOUGH TO FOLD OVER FOAM PADDING & COVER PLYWOOD BY 2".

PLYWOOD

VINYL UPHOLSTERY MATERIAL

PLYWOOD — FOAM PADDING

STAPLE LOCATION

STEP 2. FIRST - PULL MATERIAL TIGHT FROM BOTH SIDES & STAPLE NEAR CENTER. SECOND - PULL MATERIAL TIGHT FROM BOTH ENDS & STAPLE NEAR CENTER. CHECK TOP FOR WRINKLES.

STEP 3. PULL SIDES TIGHT & STAPLE FULL LENGTH.

STEP 4. PULL CORNER MATERIAL INTO A PARALLEL FOLD & STAPLE SIDES & ENDS TO CORNERS.

STEP 5. PULL CORNERS TIGHT & FOLD OVER PLYWOOD. CUT ENDS TO MATCH OVERLAP LENGTH & STAPLE IN PLACE.

Painting

A project "comes alive" when paint is applied. No project is complete until it has a high-quality paint job. Taking time to develop an attractive, durable, and protective finish is as important as welding a project.

Planning color groups that highlight features and identify specific parts makes a project professional. (Don't just paint everything black.) Add pinstripes, stickers, and decals to give a custom appearance.

Always prepare the material before painting. Remove any oil or grease with an appropriate solvent. Scrape and remove welding spatter from around weld areas. If rust is present, you should sand, wire brush, or sandblast to expose clean metal. Make sure materials are completely moisture-free. Since many projects will be subjected to severe conditions, use a high-quality primer before finish painting. Always let finishes dry completely between coats. Usually, applying several thin coats will give a more durable finish than one thick coat. Use a primer and finish paint that are compatible (usually the same brand). For finish coats, again apply several thin coats to avoid runs and drips. Always read the manufacturer's instructions on the can before painting.

Be sure to paint in a well-ventilated area and dispose of paint, solvents, rags, etc., in a safe and environmentally conscious manner.

Take pride in your paint job; it is what makes the rest of your work look great!

Remember–Paint on a project is like frosting on a cake.

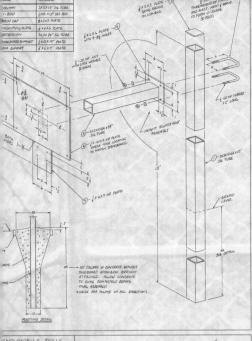

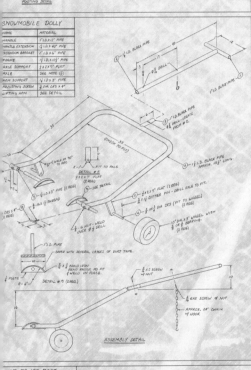

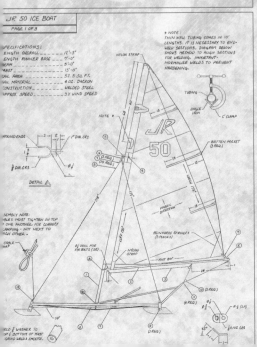

Sports Equipment

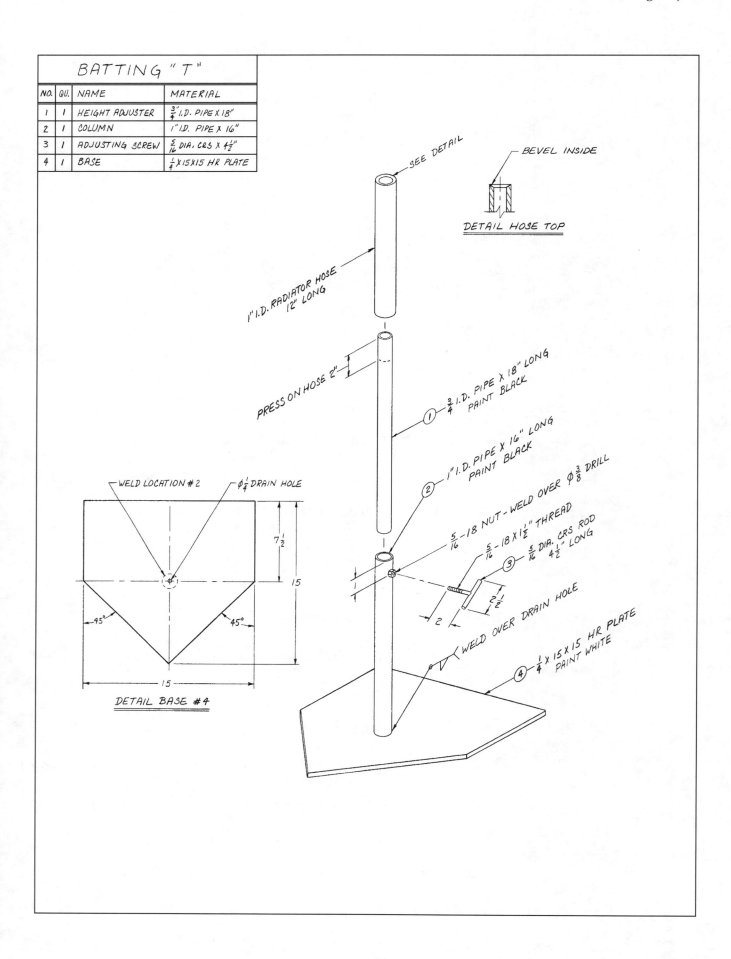

BATTING "T"

NO.	QU.	NAME	MATERIAL
1	1	HEIGHT ADJUSTER	$\frac{3}{4}$" I.D. PIPE X 18"
2	1	COLUMN	1" I.D. PIPE X 16"
3	1	ADJUSTING SCREW	$\frac{5}{16}$ DIA. CRS X 4$\frac{1}{2}$"
4	1	BASE	$\frac{1}{4}$ X 15 X 15 HR PLATE

SEE DETAIL

BEVEL INSIDE

DETAIL HOSE TOP

1" I.D. RADIATOR HOSE 12" LONG

PRESS ON HOSE 2"

① $\frac{3}{4}$" I.D. PIPE X 18" LONG PAINT BLACK

② 1" I.D. PIPE X 16" LONG PAINT BLACK

$\frac{5}{16}$ - 18 NUT - WELD OVER $\phi\frac{3}{8}$ DRILL

$\frac{5}{16}$ - 18 X 1$\frac{1}{2}$" THREAD

③ $\frac{5}{16}$ DIA. CRS ROD 4$\frac{1}{2}$" LONG

WELD OVER DRAIN HOLE

④ $\frac{1}{4}$ X 15 X 15 HR PLATE PAINT WHITE

WELD LOCATION # 2

$\phi\frac{1}{4}$ DRAIN HOLE

7$\frac{1}{2}$

15

45°   45°

15

DETAIL BASE #4

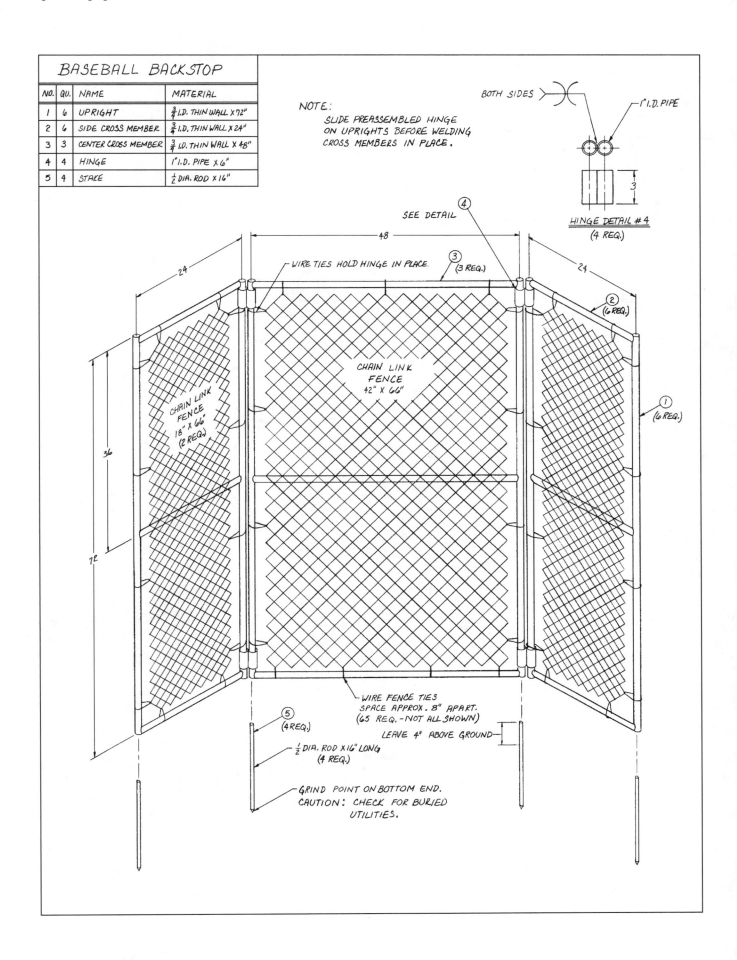

BASEBALL BACKSTOP

NO.	QU.	NAME	MATERIAL
1	6	UPRIGHT	$\frac{3}{4}$ I.D. THIN WALL X 72"
2	6	SIDE CROSS MEMBER	$\frac{3}{4}$ I.D. THIN WALL X 24"
3	3	CENTER CROSS MEMBER	$\frac{3}{4}$ I.D. THIN WALL X 48"
4	4	HINGE	1" I.D. PIPE X 6"
5	4	STAKE	$\frac{1}{2}$ DIA. ROD X 16"

NOTE:
SLIDE PREASSEMBLED HINGE
ON UPRIGHTS BEFORE WELDING
CROSS MEMBERS IN PLACE.

BOTH SIDES

1" I.D. PIPE

HINGE DETAIL #4
(4 REQ.)

3

SEE DETAIL

48

24

24

WIRE TIES HOLD HINGE IN PLACE.

③
(3 REQ.)

②
(6 REQ.)

CHAIN LINK
FENCE
42" X 66"

CHAIN LINK
FENCE
18" X 66"
(2 REQ.)

①
(6 REQ.)

36

72

WIRE FENCE TIES
SPACE APPROX. 8" APART.
(65 REQ. - NOT ALL SHOWN)

LEAVE 4" ABOVE GROUND

⑤
(4 REQ.)

$\frac{1}{2}$ DIA. ROD X 16" LONG
(4 REQ.)

GRIND POINT ON BOTTOM END.
CAUTION: CHECK FOR BURIED
UTILITIES.

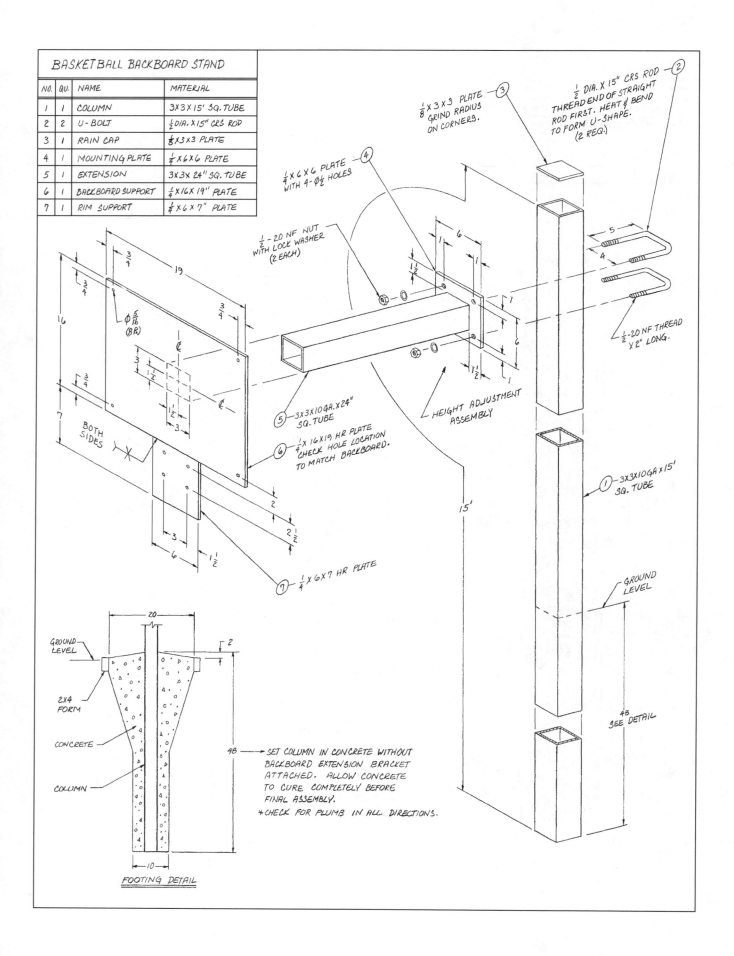

BASKETBALL BACKBOARD STAND

NO.	QU.	NAME	MATERIAL
1	1	COLUMN	3X3X15' SQ. TUBE
2	2	U-BOLT	$\frac{1}{2}$ DIA. X 15" CRS ROD
3	1	RAIN CAP	$\frac{1}{8}$ X 3 X 3 PLATE
4	1	MOUNTING PLATE	$\frac{1}{4}$ X 6 X 6 PLATE
5	1	EXTENSION	3 X 3 X 24" SQ. TUBE
6	1	BACKBOARD SUPPORT	$\frac{1}{4}$ X 16 X 19" PLATE
7	1	RIM SUPPORT	$\frac{1}{4}$ X 6 X 7" PLATE

$\frac{1}{8}$ X 3 X 3 PLATE GRIND RADIUS ON CORNERS.

$\frac{1}{2}$ DIA. X 15" CRS ROD THREAD END OF STRAIGHT ROD FIRST. HEAT & BEND TO FORM U-SHAPE. (2 REQ.)

$\frac{1}{4}$ X 6 X 6 PLATE WITH 4-$\phi\frac{1}{2}$ HOLES

$\frac{1}{2}$ - 20 NF NUT WITH LOCK WASHER (2 EACH)

$\frac{1}{2}$ - 20 NF THREAD X 2" LONG.

$\phi \frac{5}{16}$ (8 R)

HEIGHT ADJUSTMENT ASSEMBLY

BOTH SIDES

5 - 3 X 3 X 10 GA. X 24" SQ. TUBE

6 - $\frac{1}{4}$ X 16 X 19 HR PLATE CHECK HOLE LOCATION TO MATCH BACKBOARD.

1 - 3 X 3 X 10 GA. X 15' SQ. TUBE

GROUND LEVEL

7 - $\frac{1}{4}$ X 6 X 7 HR PLATE

48 SEE DETAIL

FOOTING DETAIL

GROUND LEVEL

2 X 4 FORM

CONCRETE

COLUMN

48 → SET COLUMN IN CONCRETE WITHOUT BACKBOARD EXTENSION BRACKET ATTACHED. ALLOW CONCRETE TO CURE COMPLETELY BEFORE FINAL ASSEMBLY.
* CHECK FOR PLUMB IN ALL DIRECTIONS.

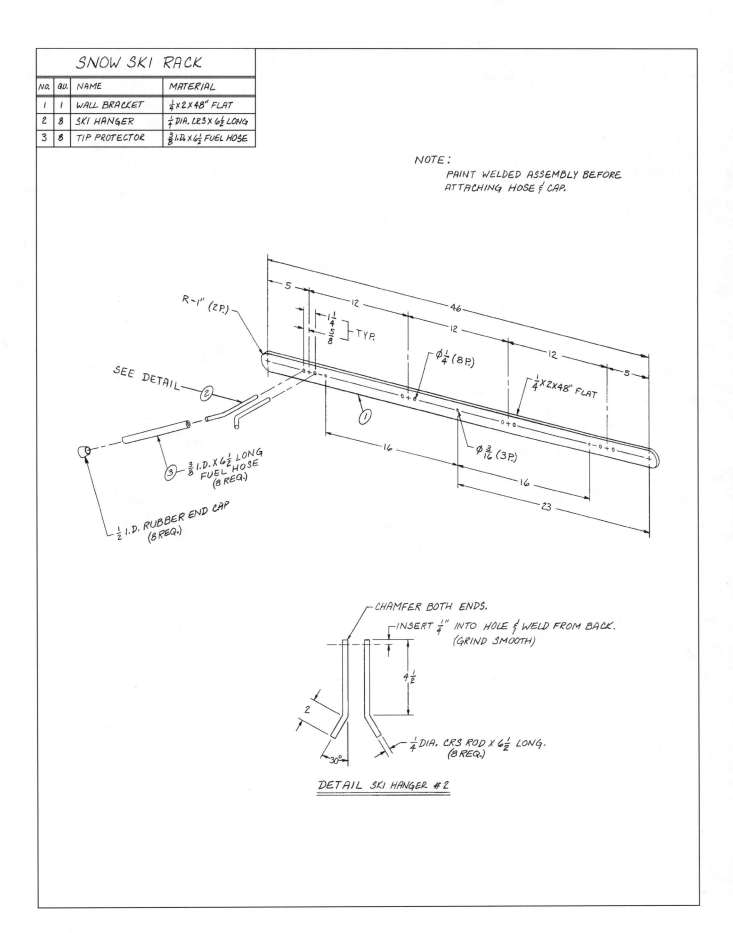

SNOW SKI RACK

NO.	QU.	NAME	MATERIAL
1	1	WALL BRACKET	$\frac{1}{4} \times 2 \times 48$" FLAT
2	8	SKI HANGER	$\frac{1}{4}$ DIA. CRS $\times 6\frac{1}{2}$ LONG
3	8	TIP PROTECTOR	$\frac{3}{8}$ I.D. $\times 6\frac{1}{2}$ FUEL HOSE

NOTE:
PAINT WELDED ASSEMBLY BEFORE
ATTACHING HOSE & CAP.

R-1" (2 P.)

SEE DETAIL ②

③ $\frac{3}{8}$ I.D. $\times 6\frac{1}{2}$ LONG
FUEL HOSE
(8 REQ.)

$\frac{1}{2}$ I.D. RUBBER END CAP
(8 REQ.)

$\frac{1}{4}$ TYP.
$\frac{5}{8}$

5

12

46

12

12

5

$\phi\frac{1}{4}$ (8 P.)

$\frac{1}{4} \times 2 \times 48$" FLAT

①

16

$\phi\frac{3}{16}$ (3 P.)

16

23

CHAMFER BOTH ENDS.

INSERT $\frac{1}{4}$" INTO HOLE & WELD FROM BACK.
(GRIND SMOOTH)

$4\frac{1}{2}$

2

30°

$\frac{1}{4}$ DIA. CRS ROD $\times 6\frac{1}{2}$ LONG.
(8 REQ.)

DETAIL SKI HANGER #2

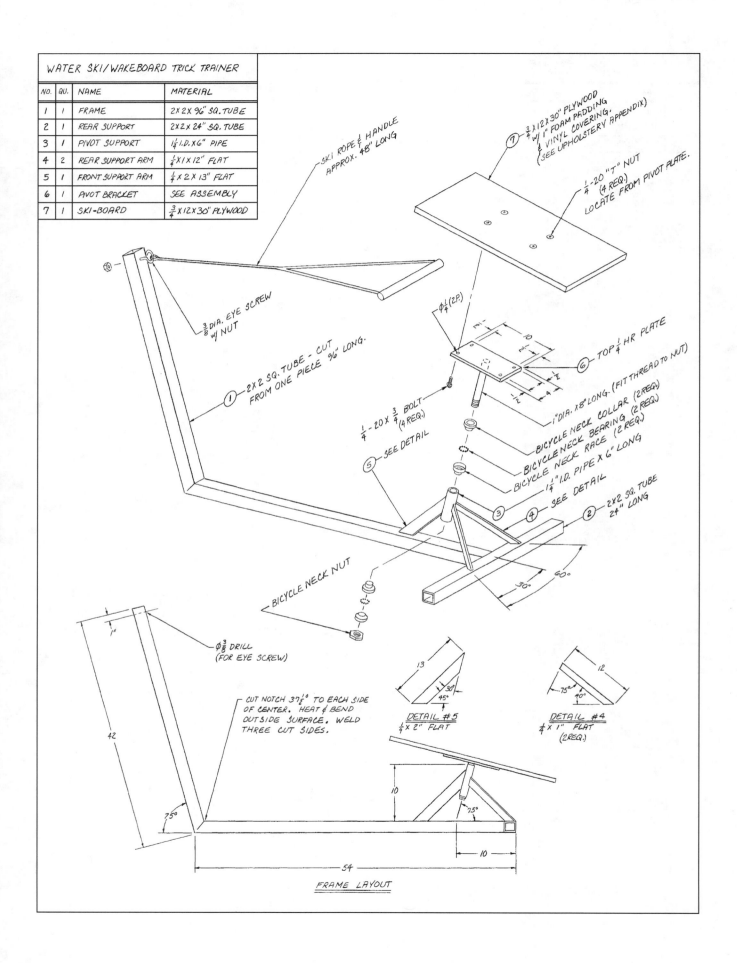

WATER SKI/WAKEBOARD TRICK TRAINER

NO.	QU.	NAME	MATERIAL
1	1	FRAME	2 X 2 X 96" SQ. TUBE
2	1	REAR SUPPORT	2 X 2 X 24" SQ. TUBE
3	1	PIVOT SUPPORT	1¼ I.D. X 6" PIPE
4	2	REAR SUPPORT ARM	¼ X 1 X 12" FLAT
5	1	FRONT SUPPORT ARM	¼ X 2 X 13" FLAT
6	1	PIVOT BRACKET	SEE ASSEMBLY
7	1	SKI-BOARD	¾ X 12 X 30" PLYWOOD

SKI ROPE & HANDLE
APPROX. 48" LONG

¾ X 12 X 30" PLYWOOD
w/ 1" FOAM PADDING
& VINYL COVERING.
(SEE UPHOLSTERY APPENDIX)

¼-20 "T" NUT
(4 REQ.)
LOCATE FROM PIVOT PLATE.

⅜ DIA. EYE SCREW
w/ NUT

2 X 2 SQ. TUBE - CUT
FROM ONE PIECE 96" LONG.

ϕ¼ (2 P.)

TOP ¼ HR PLATE

1" DIA. X 8" LONG. (FIT THREAD TO NUT)

¼-20 X ¾ BOLT
(4 REQ.)
SEE DETAIL

BICYCLE NECK COLLAR (2 REQ.)
BICYCLE NECK BEARING (2 REQ.)
BICYCLE NECK RACE (2 REQ.)
1¼" I.D. PIPE X 6" LONG
SEE DETAIL

2 X 2 SQ. TUBE
24" LONG

30°   60°

BICYCLE NECK NUT

ϕ⅜ DRILL
(FOR EYE SCREW)

42

75°

CUT NOTCH 37½° TO EACH SIDE
OF CENTER. HEAT & BEND
OUTSIDE SURFACE. WELD
THREE CUT SIDES.

1"

13
30°
45°
DETAIL #5
¼ X 2" FLAT

12
75°
40°
DETAIL #4
¼ X 1" FLAT
(2 REQ.)

10

75°

10

54

FRAME LAYOUT

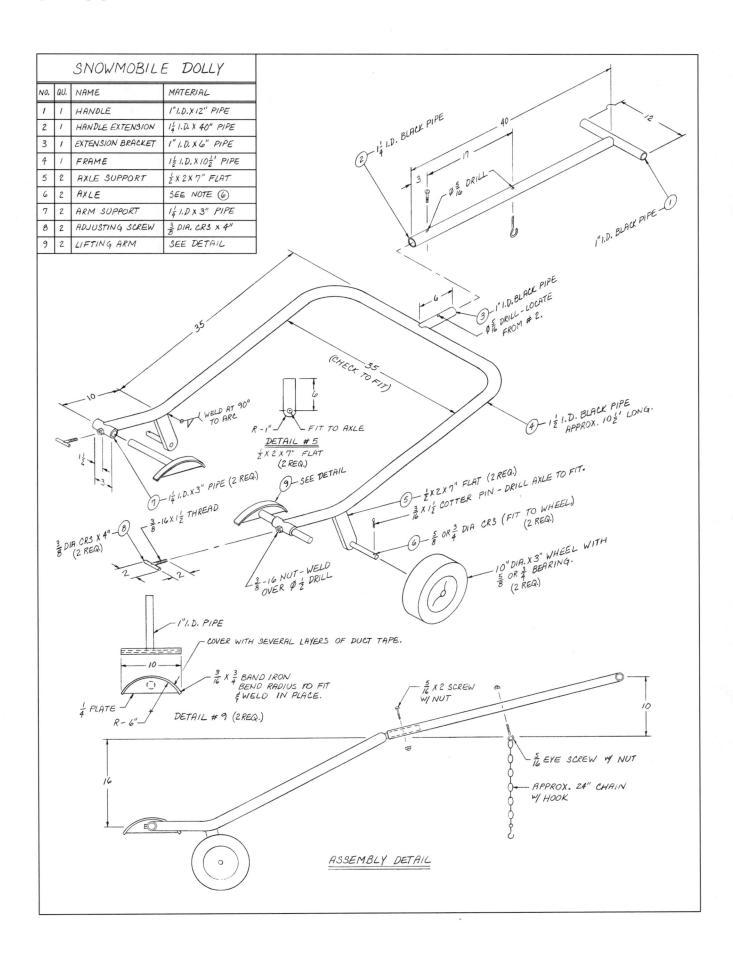

SNOWMOBILE DOLLY

NO.	QU.	NAME	MATERIAL
1	1	HANDLE	1" I.D. X 12" PIPE
2	1	HANDLE EXTENSION	1¼ I.D. X 40" PIPE
3	1	EXTENSION BRACKET	1" I.D. X 6" PIPE
4	1	FRAME	1½ I.D. X 10½' PIPE
5	2	AXLE SUPPORT	½ X 2 X 7" FLAT
6	2	AXLE	SEE NOTE ⑥
7	2	ARM SUPPORT	1¼ I.D X 3" PIPE
8	2	ADJUSTING SCREW	⅜ DIA. CRS X 4"
9	2	LIFTING ARM	SEE DETAIL

DETAIL #5
½ X 2 X 7" FLAT
(2 REQ.)

DETAIL #9 (2 REQ.)

ASSEMBLY DETAIL

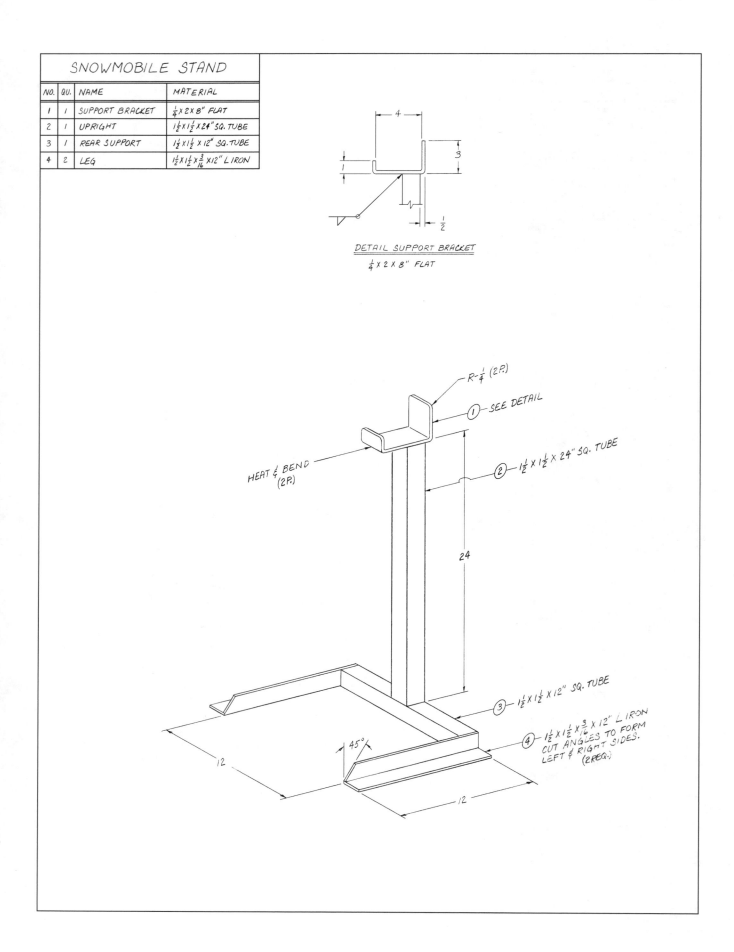

SNOWMOBILE STAND

NO.	QU.	NAME	MATERIAL
1	1	SUPPORT BRACKET	$\frac{1}{4} \times 2 \times 8''$ FLAT
2	1	UPRIGHT	$1\frac{1}{2} \times 1\frac{1}{2} \times 24''$ SQ. TUBE
3	1	REAR SUPPORT	$1\frac{1}{2} \times 1\frac{1}{2} \times 12''$ SQ. TUBE
4	2	LEG	$1\frac{1}{2} \times 1\frac{1}{2} \times \frac{3}{16} \times 12''$ L IRON

DETAIL SUPPORT BRACKET
$\frac{1}{4} \times 2 \times 8''$ FLAT

4

3

1

$\frac{1}{2}$

R-$\frac{1}{4}$ (2 P.)

① — SEE DETAIL

② — $1\frac{1}{2} \times 1\frac{1}{2} \times 24''$ SQ. TUBE

HEAT & BEND
(2 P.)

24

③ — $1\frac{1}{2} \times 1\frac{1}{2} \times 12''$ SQ. TUBE

④ — $1\frac{1}{2} \times 1\frac{1}{2} \times \frac{3}{16} \times 12''$ L IRON
CUT ANGLES TO FORM
LEFT & RIGHT SIDES.
(2 REQ.)

12

45°

12

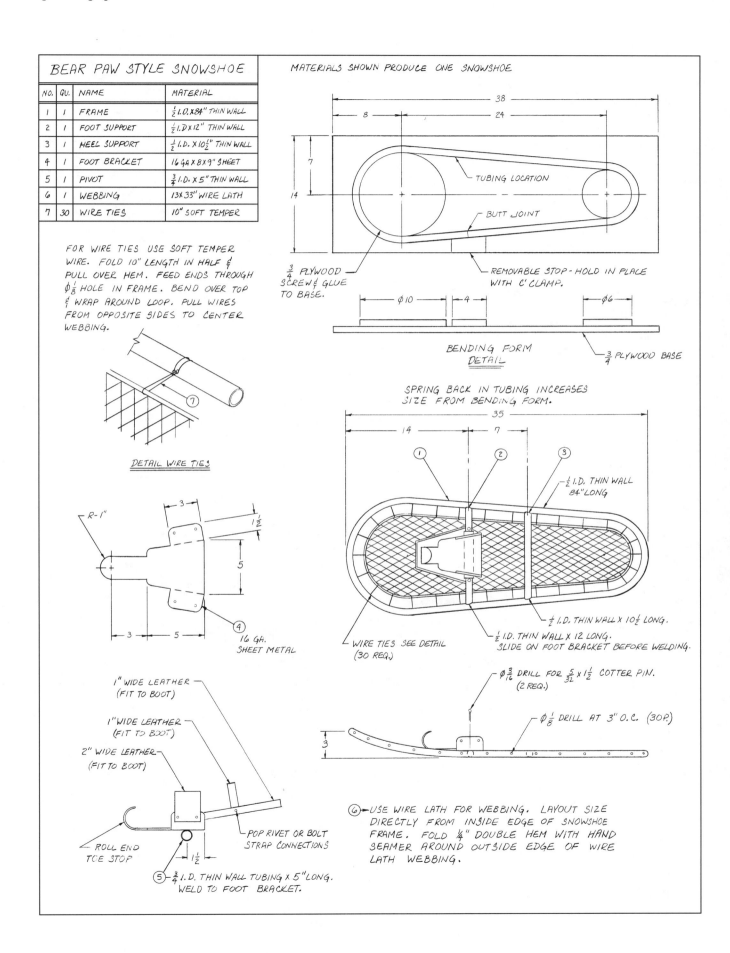

BEAR PAW STYLE SNOWSHOE

NO.	QU.	NAME	MATERIAL
1	1	FRAME	$\frac{1}{2}$ I.D. X 84" THIN WALL
2	1	FOOT SUPPORT	$\frac{1}{2}$ I.D X 12" THIN WALL
3	1	HEEL SUPPORT	$\frac{1}{2}$ I.D. X 10$\frac{1}{2}$" THIN WALL
4	1	FOOT BRACKET	16 GA X 8 X 9" SHEET
5	1	PIVOT	$\frac{3}{4}$ I.D. X 5" THIN WALL
6	1	WEBBING	13 X 33" WIRE LATH
7	30	WIRE TIES	10" SOFT TEMPER

FOR WIRE TIES USE SOFT TEMPER WIRE. FOLD 10" LENGTH IN HALF & PULL OVER HEM. FEED ENDS THROUGH $\phi\frac{1}{8}$ HOLE IN FRAME. BEND OVER TOP & WRAP AROUND LOOP. PULL WIRES FROM OPPOSITE SIDES TO CENTER WEBBING.

DETAIL WIRE TIES

MATERIALS SHOWN PRODUCE ONE SNOWSHOE

38
8
24
7
14

TUBING LOCATION
BUTT JOINT
$\frac{3}{4}$ PLYWOOD SCREW & GLUE TO BASE.
REMOVABLE STOP - HOLD IN PLACE WITH C'CLAMP.

ϕ10
4
ϕ6

BENDING FORM DETAIL
$\frac{3}{4}$ PLYWOOD BASE

SPRING BACK IN TUBING INCREASES SIZE FROM BENDING FORM.

35
14
7

① ② ③

$\frac{1}{2}$ I.D. THIN WALL 84" LONG

$\frac{1}{2}$ I.D. THIN WALL X 10$\frac{1}{2}$ LONG.
$\frac{1}{2}$ I.D. THIN WALL X 12 LONG. SLIDE ON FOOT BRACKET BEFORE WELDING.

WIRE TIES SEE DETAIL (30 REQ.)

R-1"
3
1$\frac{1}{2}$
5
3
5
④ 16 GA. SHEET METAL

$\phi\frac{3}{16}$ DRILL FOR $\frac{5}{32}$ X 1$\frac{1}{2}$ COTTER PIN. (2 REQ.)
$\phi\frac{1}{8}$ DRILL AT 3" O.C. (30 P.)
3

1" WIDE LEATHER (FIT TO BOOT)
1" WIDE LEATHER (FIT TO BOOT)
2" WIDE LEATHER (FIT TO BOOT)

ROLL END TOE STOP
POP RIVET OR BOLT STRAP CONNECTIONS
1$\frac{1}{2}$
⑤ $\frac{3}{4}$ I.D. THIN WALL TUBING X 5" LONG. WELD TO FOOT BRACKET.

⑥ USE WIRE LATH FOR WEBBING. LAYOUT SIZE DIRECTLY FROM INSIDE EDGE OF SNOWSHOE FRAME. FOLD $\frac{1}{4}$" DOUBLE HEM WITH HAND SEAMER AROUND OUTSIDE EDGE OF WIRE LATH WEBBING.

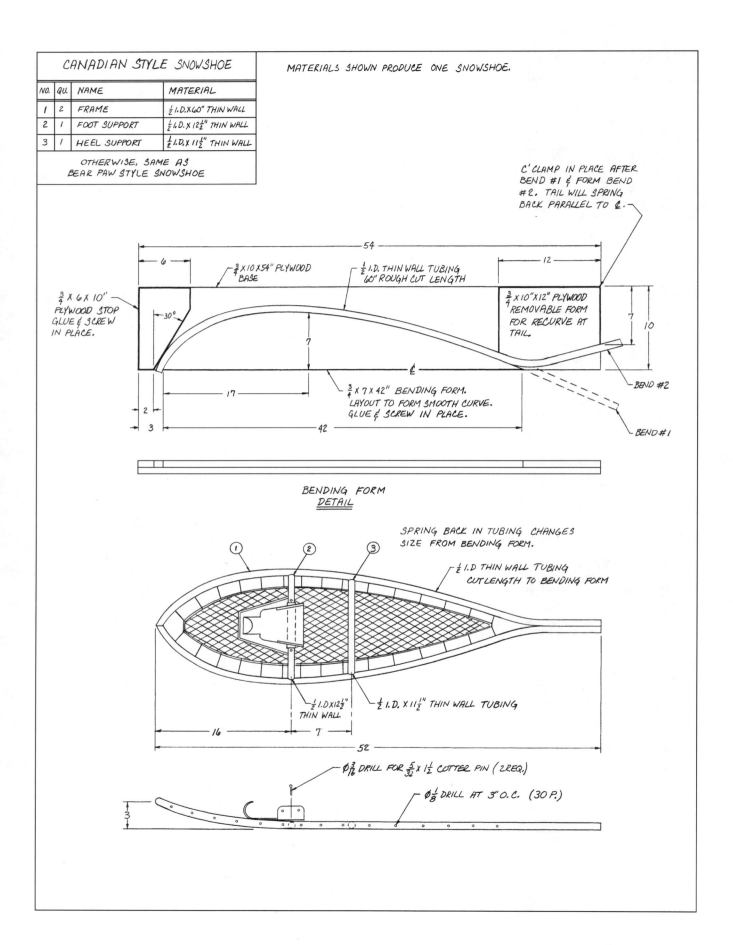

CANADIAN STYLE SNOWSHOE

NO.	QU.	NAME	MATERIAL
1	2	FRAME	$\frac{1}{2}$ I.D. X 60" THIN WALL
2	1	FOOT SUPPORT	$\frac{1}{2}$ I.D. X 12$\frac{1}{2}$" THIN WALL
3	1	HEEL SUPPORT	$\frac{1}{2}$ I.D. X 11$\frac{1}{2}$" THIN WALL

OTHERWISE, SAME AS
BEAR PAW STYLE SNOWSHOE

MATERIALS SHOWN PRODUCE ONE SNOWSHOE.

C'CLAMP IN PLACE AFTER
BEND #1 & FORM BEND
#2. TAIL WILL SPRING
BACK PARALLEL TO ₵.

54

6

$\frac{3}{4}$ X 10 X 54" PLYWOOD
BASE

$\frac{1}{2}$ I.D. THIN WALL TUBING
60" ROUGH CUT LENGTH

12

$\frac{3}{4}$ X 6 X 10"
PLYWOOD STOP
GLUE & SCREW
IN PLACE.

30°

$\frac{3}{4}$ X 10" X 12" PLYWOOD
REMOVABLE FORM
FOR RECURVE AT
TAIL.

7

7

10

BEND #2

17

$\frac{3}{4}$ X 7 X 42" BENDING FORM.
LAYOUT TO FORM SMOOTH CURVE.
GLUE & SCREW IN PLACE.

₵

2

3

42

BEND #1

BENDING FORM
DETAIL

SPRING BACK IN TUBING CHANGES
SIZE FROM BENDING FORM.

$\frac{1}{2}$ I.D THIN WALL TUBING
CUT LENGTH TO BENDING FORM

① ② ③

$\frac{1}{2}$ I.D. X 12$\frac{1}{2}$"
THIN WALL

$\frac{1}{2}$ I.D. X 11$\frac{1}{2}$" THIN WALL TUBING

16

7

52

$\emptyset \frac{3}{16}$ DRILL FOR $\frac{5}{32}$ X 1$\frac{1}{2}$ COTTER PIN (2 REQ.)

$\emptyset \frac{1}{8}$ DRILL AT 3" O.C. (30 P.)

3

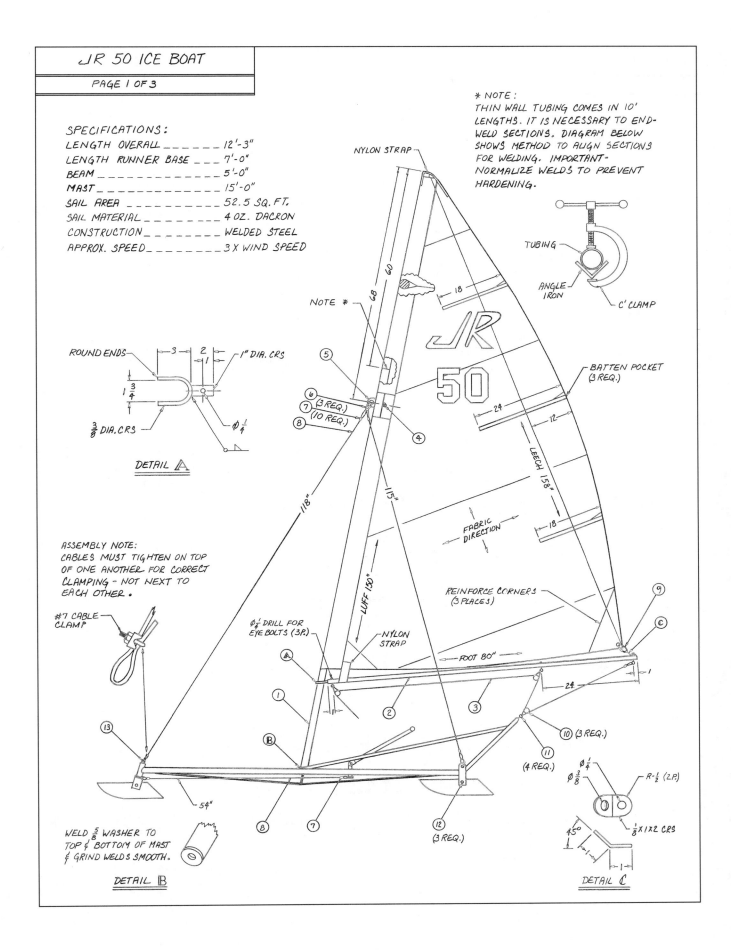

JR 50 ICE BOAT

PAGE 1 OF 3

SPECIFICATIONS:
LENGTH OVERALL _____ 12'-3"
LENGTH RUNNER BASE ___ 7'-0"
BEAM _____ 5'-0"
MAST _____ 15'-0"
SAIL AREA _____ 52.5 SQ.FT.
SAIL MATERIAL _____ 4 OZ. DACRON
CONSTRUCTION_____ WELDED STEEL
APPROX. SPEED_____ 3 X WIND SPEED

* NOTE:
THIN WALL TUBING COMES IN 10'
LENGTHS. IT IS NECESSARY TO END-
WELD SECTIONS. DIAGRAM BELOW
SHOWS METHOD TO ALIGN SECTIONS
FOR WELDING. IMPORTANT-
NORMALIZE WELDS TO PREVENT
HARDENING.

NYLON STRAP

TUBING

ANGLE IRON

C CLAMP

ROUND ENDS
1" DIA. CRS
3/8 DIA. CRS
Ø 1/4

DETAIL A

BATTEN POCKET
(3 REQ.)

LEECH 158"

FABRIC DIRECTION

ASSEMBLY NOTE:
CABLES MUST TIGHTEN ON TOP
OF ONE ANOTHER FOR CORRECT
CLAMPING - NOT NEXT TO
EACH OTHER.

#7 CABLE CLAMP

REINFORCE CORNERS
(3 PLACES)

Ø 1/2 DRILL FOR
EYE BOLTS (3 P.)

NYLON STRAP

FOOT 80"

LUFF 150"

24

10 (3 REQ.)

11
(4 REQ.)

Ø 1/4
Ø 3/8
R-1/2 (2.P.)
1/8 X 1 X 2 CRS
45°

WELD 5/8 WASHER TO
TOP & BOTTOM OF MAST
& GRIND WELDS SMOOTH.

54"

12
(3 REQ.)

DETAIL B

DETAIL C

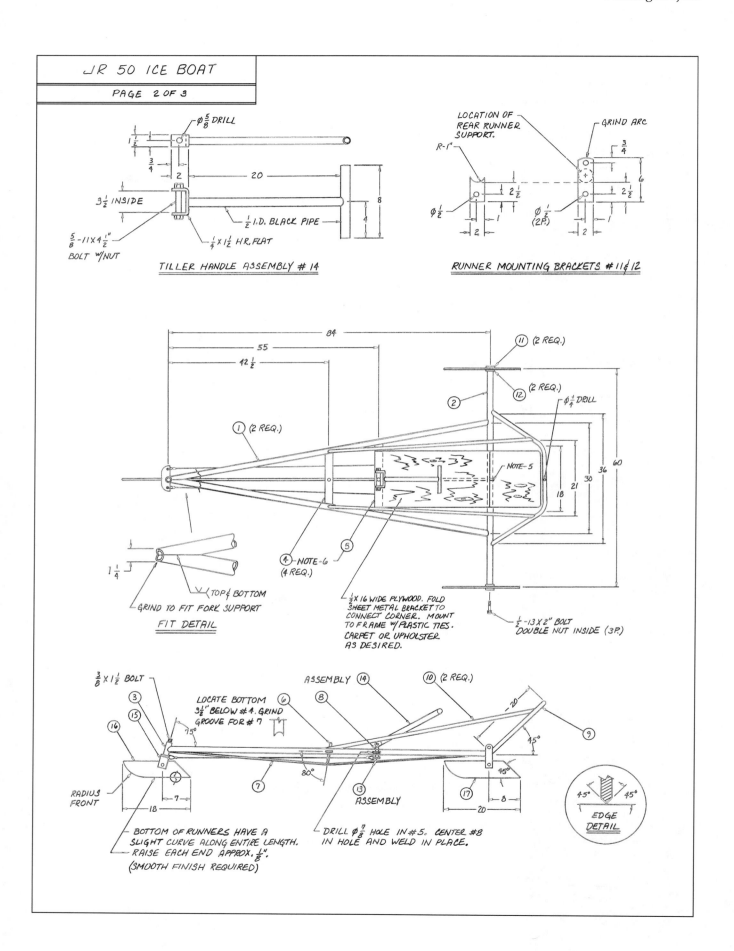

JR 50 ICE BOAT
PAGE 2 OF 3

$\phi \frac{5}{8}$ DRILL

$\frac{1}{2}$ I.D. BLACK PIPE

$\frac{1}{4} \times 1\frac{1}{2}$ HR. FLAT

$3\frac{1}{2}$ INSIDE

$\frac{5}{8}$-11 X 4 $\frac{1}{2}$" BOLT W/NUT

TILLER HANDLE ASSEMBLY # 14

LOCATION OF REAR RUNNER SUPPORT.

GRIND ARC

R-1"

$\phi \frac{1}{2}$

$\phi \frac{1}{2}$ (2 P.)

RUNNER MOUNTING BRACKETS #11 & 12

$\phi \frac{1}{4}$ DRILL

NOTE-5

(1) (2 REQ.)

(2)

(11) (2 REQ.)

(12) (2 REQ.)

(4) NOTE-6 (4 REQ.)

(5)

GRIND TO FIT FORK SUPPORT

FIT DETAIL

$\frac{1}{2}$ X 16 WIDE PLYWOOD. FOLD SHEET METAL BRACKET TO CONNECT CORNER. MOUNT TO FRAME W/ PLASTIC TIES. CARPET OR UPHOLSTER AS DESIRED.

$\frac{1}{2}$ -13 X 2" BOLT DOUBLE NUT INSIDE (3 P.)

$\frac{3}{8}$ X 1 $\frac{1}{2}$ BOLT

(3)

(15)

(16)

LOCATE BOTTOM 3 $\frac{1}{2}$" BELOW #4. GRIND GROOVE FOR #7

ASSEMBLY (14)

(6)

(8)

(10) (2 REQ.)

(9)

RADIUS FRONT

(7)

(13) ASSEMBLY

ASSEMBLY

(17)

BOTTOM OF RUNNERS HAVE A SLIGHT CURVE ALONG ENTIRE LENGTH. RAISE EACH END APPROX. $\frac{1}{8}$". (SMOOTH FINISH REQUIRED)

DRILL $\phi \frac{7}{8}$ HOLE IN #5. CENTER #8 IN HOLE AND WELD IN PLACE.

EDGE DETAIL

JR 50 ICE BOAT

PAGE 3 OF 3

MATERIALS FROM PAGE 1

NO.	QU.	NAME	MATERIAL
1	1	MAST	$1\frac{1}{2}$ I.D. X 15' THIN WALL
2	1	BOOM	1" I.D. X 7'-3" THIN WALL
3	1	SHEET LINE	$\frac{3}{8}$ DIA. ROPE X 15'
4	1	CROWN NUT	$\frac{3}{8}$ -16 THREAD
5	1	EYE (FORGED)	$\frac{3}{8}$ -16 THREAD
6	3	CHAIN LINK	$\frac{3}{8}$ DIA.
7	10	CABLE CLAMPS	$\frac{1}{4}$ -20 THREAD
8	50'	CABLE	$\frac{1}{8}$ BRAIDED STEEL
9	1	CHAIN LINK	$\frac{1}{4}$ DIA.
10	3	BLOCK PULLEY	$1\frac{1}{2}$ DIA. WHEEL
11	4	EYE BOLT	$\frac{1}{4}$ DIA.
12	3	BOLT & DOUBLE NUT	$\frac{1}{2}$ -13 X 2"
13		BOLT & NUT	$\frac{3}{8}$ -16 X $1\frac{1}{2}$"

MATERIALS FROM PAGE 2

NO.	QU.	NAME	MATERIAL
1	2	SIDE	$1\frac{1}{4}$ I.D. X 85" PIPE
2	1	REAR RUNNER SUPT.	$1\frac{1}{2}$ I.D. X 60" PIPE
3	1	FORK SUPPORT	1" I.D. X 4" PIPE
4	4	MAST SUPPORT	$\frac{1}{4}$ X 2 X 14" HR FLAT
5	1	STEERING-SEAT SUPT.	$\frac{1}{4}$ X 2 X 19" HR FLAT
6	1	MAST STEP	$\frac{1}{2}$ DIA. X 6" CRS
7	1	TENSION ROD	$\frac{3}{8}$ DIA. X 86" CRS
8	1	TILLER PIVOT	$\frac{1}{2}$ I.D. X 3" PIPE
9	1	SEAT BACK SUPT.	$\frac{1}{2}$ I.D. X 60" PIPE
10	2	SEAT BACK BRACE	$\frac{1}{2}$ I.D. X 53" PIPE
11	2	OUTER BRACKET	$\frac{1}{4}$ X 2 X 6" HR FLAT
12	2	INNER BRACKET	$\frac{1}{4}$ X 2 X 3" HR FLAT
13	1	STEERING DRIVE	SEE DETAIL PG. 3
14	1	TILLER HANDLE	SEE DETAIL PG. 2
15	1	STEERING FORK	SEE DETAIL PG. 3
16	1	FRONT RUNNER	$\frac{1}{4}$ X 4 X 18" HR FLAT
17	2	REAR RUNNER	$\frac{1}{4}$ X 4 X 20" HR FLAT

NOTES:

1. WHEN ICE BOATING ALWAYS WEAR A SAFETY HELMET & CHECK FOR SAFE ICE CONDITIONS BEFORE SAILING.
2. ICE BOAT RIGGING IS SUBJECT TO TREMENDOUS STRESS. ALWAYS CHECK ALL CONNECTIONS & FASTENERS BEFORE SAILING.
3. SIDE SHROUDS 115" SHOULD HAVE SLACK.
4. STEERING CABLES #8 SHOULD NOT BE TAUT OR STEERING WILL BE DIFFICULT.
5. TENSION ROD INSTALLATION. DRILL $\emptyset\frac{3}{8}$ HOLE THROUGH #2. WELD #7 TO FRONT OF FRAME & THROUGH $\emptyset\frac{3}{8}$ HOLE. DRAW TENSION ROD TIGHT WITH CROW BAR & WELD IN PLACE TO #2.
6. MAST SUPPORT #4 & SEAT SUPPORT #5, LAY OUT EXACT LENGTH & ANGLES FROM SIDES #1.
7. SNUG NUTS ON RUNNER BRACKETS SO RUNNERS CAN SWIVEL UP & DOWN BUT HAVE NO SIDE WOBBLE.
8. LUBRICATE STEERING FORK WITH GREASE.
9. PART # 5 MAST EYE - MUST BE EXTREMELY STRONG. BOAT BOW EYE WORKS WELL.
10. PART #13 $\frac{3}{8}$ -16 X $1\frac{1}{2}$" BOLT - HOLDS STEERING FORK IN PLACE & IS LOWER CONNECTION OF FORE STAY.
11. BATTENS - $\frac{1}{8}$ X $\frac{3}{4}$ OAK. LENGTH SAME AS POCKET.
12. ADD 8" TO BOTH ENDS OF RIGGING & STEERING CABLES TO FORM LOOPS.
13. WELD LOOP IN ALL EYE SCREWS CLOSED.
14. SAIL CAN BE STORED BY ROLLING ON MAST.

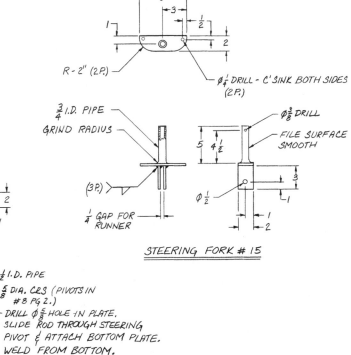

STEERING FORK # 15

STEERING DRIVE # 13

NO.	QU.	NAME	MATERIAL					
		DEER HUNTING TREE STAND		4	2	PIVOT ARM	$\frac{3}{16} \times \frac{3}{4} \times 10\frac{3}{4}$" BAND IRON
				5	2	SIDE FRAME	1X1X34½" SQ. TUBE
				6	1	END FRAME	1X1X20" SQ. TUBE
1	1	PLATFORM	½ X 20 X 24" PLYWOOD	7	2	CENTER SUPPORT	1X1X18" SQ. TUBE
2	2	ADJUSTING ARM	1X1X42" SQ.TUBE	8	1	BOTTOM CLAMP	1X1X$\frac{3}{16}$X28" L IRON
3	1	TOP CLAMP	1X1X$\frac{3}{16}$X30" L IRON	9	4	PIVOT BRACKET	$\frac{3}{16} \times \frac{3}{4} \times 2\frac{3}{8}$" BAND IRON

NOTE:
$\phi \frac{5}{16}$ DRILL ALL HOLES.
(UNLESS OTHERWISE NOTED)

WARNING:
ALWAYS WEAR A SAFETY BELT OR
HARNESS WHEN HUNTING FROM
A TREE STAND.

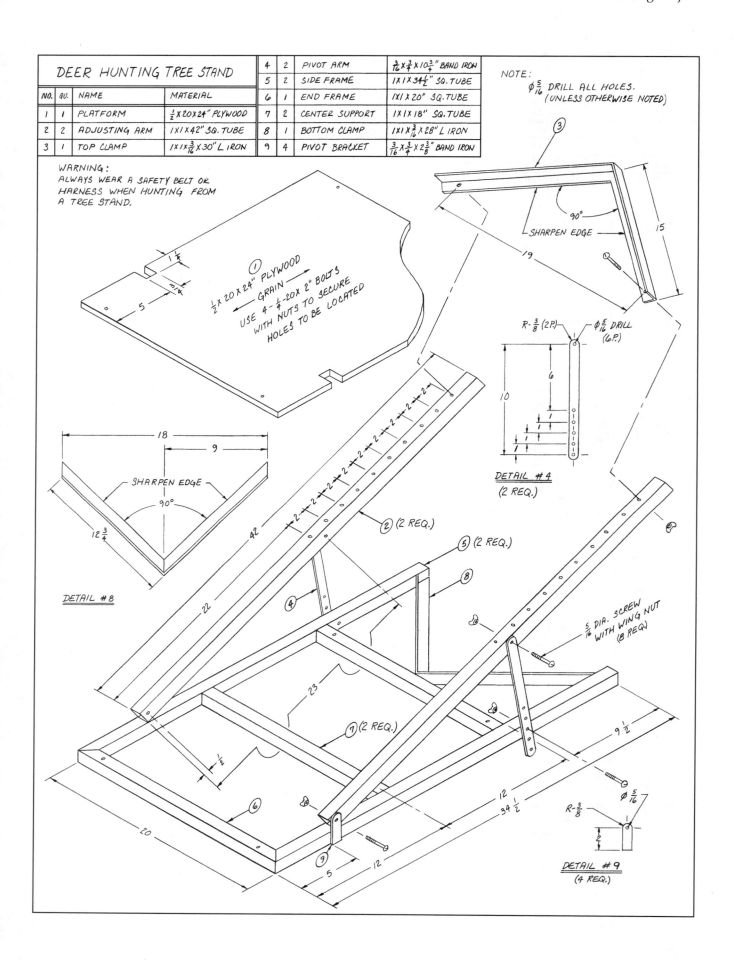

DETAIL #8

DETAIL #4
(2 REQ.)

DETAIL #9
(4 REQ.)

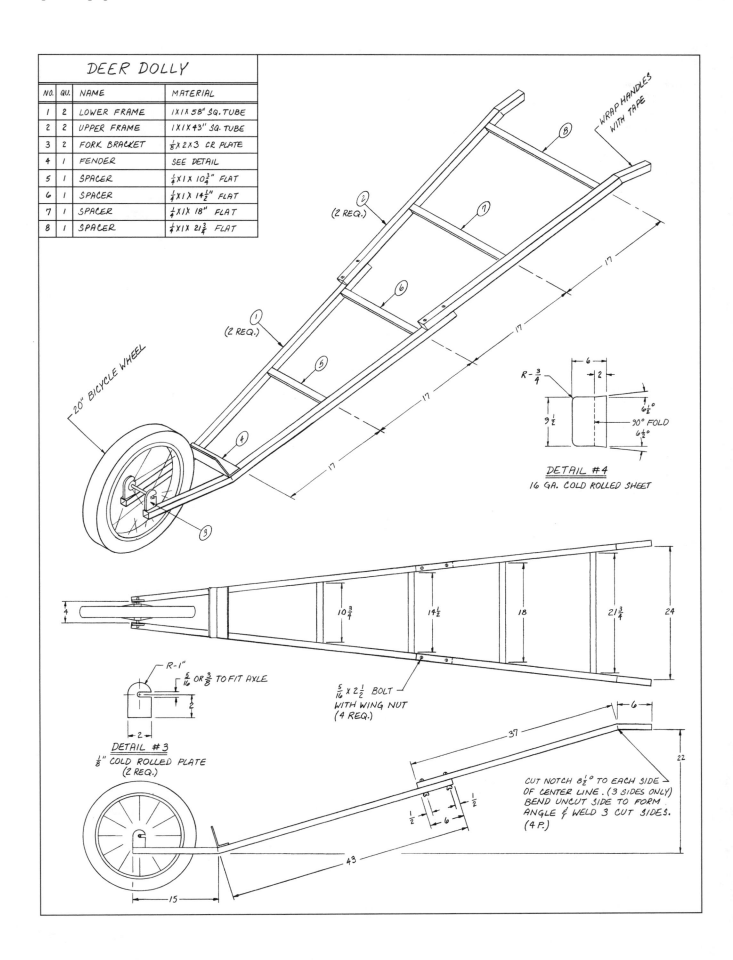

DEER DOLLY

NO.	QU.	NAME	MATERIAL
1	2	LOWER FRAME	1 X 1 X 58" SQ. TUBE
2	2	UPPER FRAME	1 X 1 X 43" SQ. TUBE
3	2	FORK BRACKET	$\frac{1}{8}$ X 2 X 3 CR PLATE
4	1	FENDER	SEE DETAIL
5	1	SPACER	$\frac{1}{4}$ X 1 X 10$\frac{3}{4}$" FLAT
6	1	SPACER	$\frac{1}{4}$ X 1 X 14$\frac{1}{2}$" FLAT
7	1	SPACER	$\frac{1}{4}$ X 1 X 18" FLAT
8	1	SPACER	$\frac{1}{4}$ X 1 X 21$\frac{3}{4}$" FLAT

WRAP HANDLES WITH TAPE

8

(2 REQ.)

7

6

5

4

3

(2 REQ.)

17

17

17

20" BICYCLE WHEEL

R - $\frac{3}{4}$

6

2

9$\frac{1}{2}$

6$\frac{1}{2}$°

90° FOLD

6$\frac{1}{2}$°

DETAIL #4
16 GA. COLD ROLLED SHEET

10$\frac{3}{4}$ 14$\frac{1}{2}$ 18   21$\frac{3}{4}$ 24

4

R - 1"

$\frac{5}{16}$ OR $\frac{3}{8}$ TO FIT AXLE

2

2

DETAIL #3
$\frac{1}{8}$" COLD ROLLED PLATE
(2 REQ.)

$\frac{5}{16}$ X 2$\frac{1}{2}$ BOLT
WITH WING NUT
(4 REQ.)

37

6

22

$\frac{1}{2}$ $\frac{1}{2}$

$\frac{1}{2}$ 6

CUT NOTCH 8$\frac{1}{2}$° TO EACH SIDE
OF CENTER LINE. (3 SIDES ONLY)
BEND UNCUT SIDE TO FORM
ANGLE & WELD 3 CUT SIDES.
(4 P.)

43

15

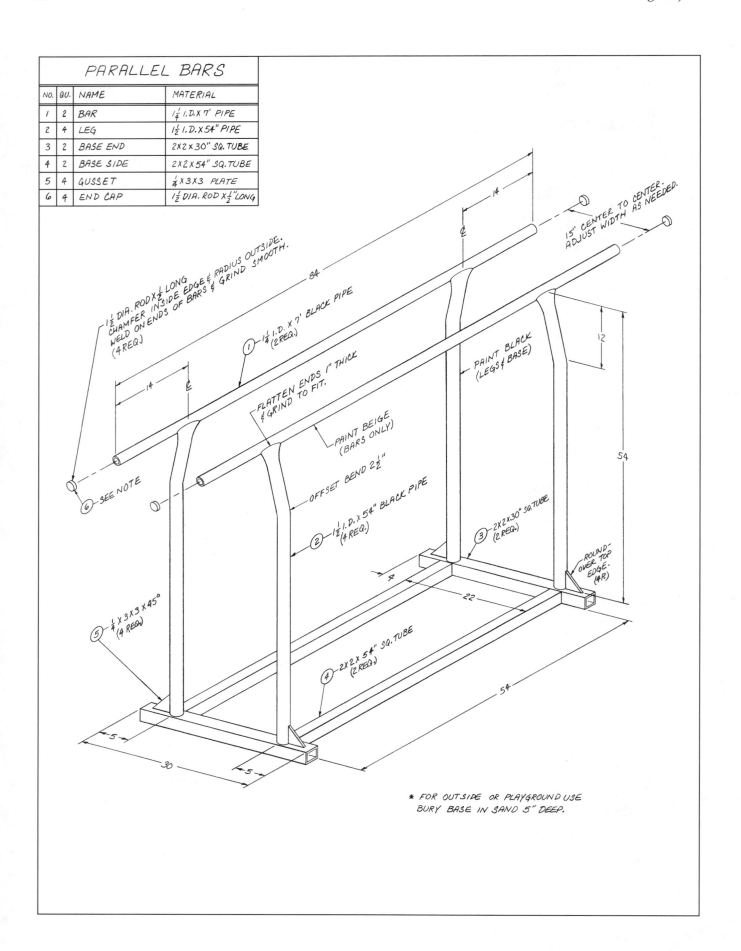

PARALLEL BARS

NO.	QU.	NAME	MATERIAL
1	2	BAR	$1\frac{1}{4}$ I.D. X 7' PIPE
2	4	LEG	$1\frac{1}{2}$ I.D. X 54" PIPE
3	2	BASE END	2X2X30" SQ. TUBE
4	2	BASE SIDE	2X2X54" SQ. TUBE
5	4	GUSSET	$\frac{1}{4}$ X 3X3 PLATE
6	4	END CAP	$1\frac{1}{2}$ DIA. ROD X$\frac{1}{2}$" LONG

$1\frac{1}{2}$ DIA. ROD X$\frac{1}{2}$ LONG
CHAMFER INSIDE EDGE & RADIUS OUTSIDE.
WELD ON ENDS OF BARS & GRIND SMOOTH.
(4 REQ.)

15" CENTER TO CENTER.
ADJUST WIDTH AS NEEDED.

14

84

① $1\frac{1}{4}$ I.D. X 7' BLACK PIPE
(2 REQ.)

PAINT BLACK
(LEGS & BASE)

12

FLATTEN ENDS 1" THICK
& GRIND TO FIT.

PAINT BEIGE
(BARS ONLY)

14

OFFSET BEND $2\frac{1}{2}$"

SEE NOTE

⑥

② $1\frac{1}{2}$ I.D. X 54" BLACK PIPE
(4 REQ.)

③ 2X2X30" SQ.TUBE
(2 REQ.)

54

ROUND
OVER TOP
EDGE.
(4 P.)

8

22

⑤ $\frac{1}{4}$ X 3 X 3 X 45°
(4 REQ.)

④ 2X2X54" SQ. TUBE
(2 REQ.)

54

5

30

5

* FOR OUTSIDE OR PLAYGROUND USE
BURY BASE IN SAND 5" DEEP.

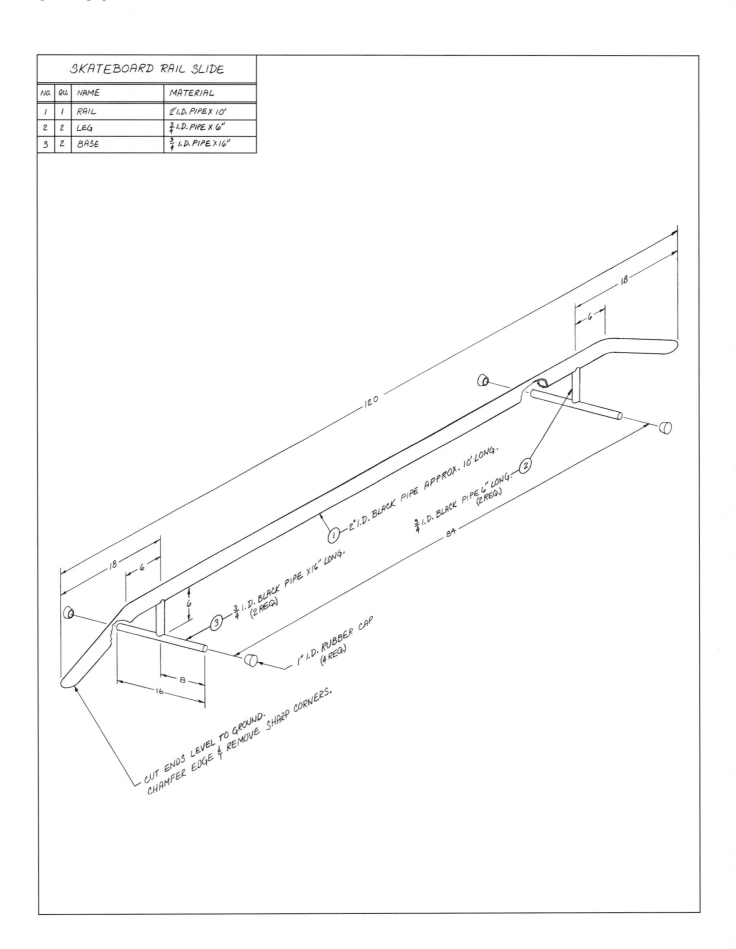

SKATEBOARD RAIL SLIDE

NO.	QU.	NAME	MATERIAL
1	1	RAIL	2" I.D. PIPE X 10'
2	2	LEG	$\frac{3}{4}$ I.D. PIPE X 6"
3	2	BASE	$\frac{3}{4}$ I.D. PIPE X 16"

120

18

6

2 — $\frac{3}{4}$ I.D. BLACK PIPE 6" LONG. (2 REQ.)

1 — 2" I.D. BLACK PIPE APPROX. 10' LONG.

84

18

6

6

3 — $\frac{3}{4}$ I.D. BLACK PIPE X 16" LONG. (2 REQ.)

1" I.D. RUBBER CAP (4 REQ.)

8

16

CUT ENDS LEVEL TO GROUND.
CHAMFER EDGE & REMOVE SHARP CORNERS.

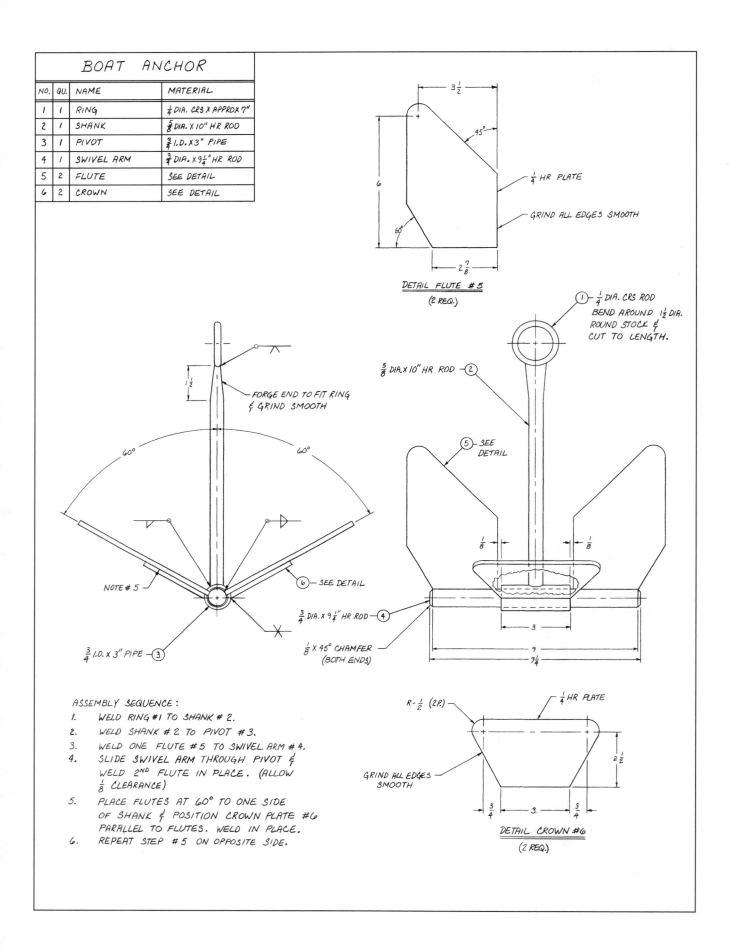

BOAT ANCHOR

NO.	QU.	NAME	MATERIAL
1	1	RING	$\frac{1}{4}$ DIA. CRS X APPROX 7"
2	1	SHANK	$\frac{5}{8}$ DIA. X 10" HR ROD
3	1	PIVOT	$\frac{3}{4}$ I.D. X 3" PIPE
4	1	SWIVEL ARM	$\frac{3}{4}$ DIA. X $9\frac{1}{4}$" HR ROD
5	2	FLUTE	SEE DETAIL
6	2	CROWN	SEE DETAIL

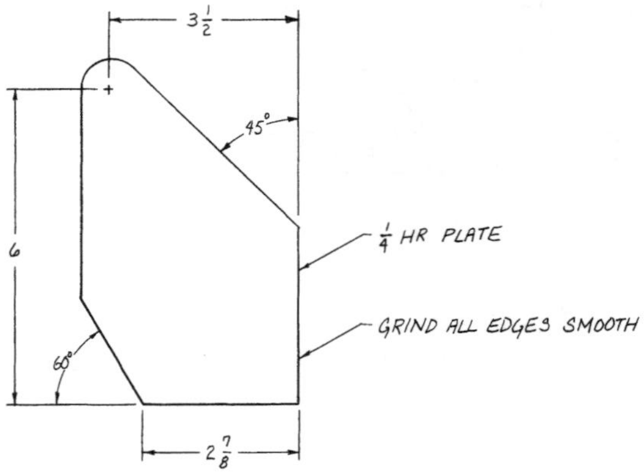
3 1/2
45°
6
60°
1/4 HR PLATE
GRIND ALL EDGES SMOOTH
2 7/8

DETAIL FLUTE #5
(2 REQ.)

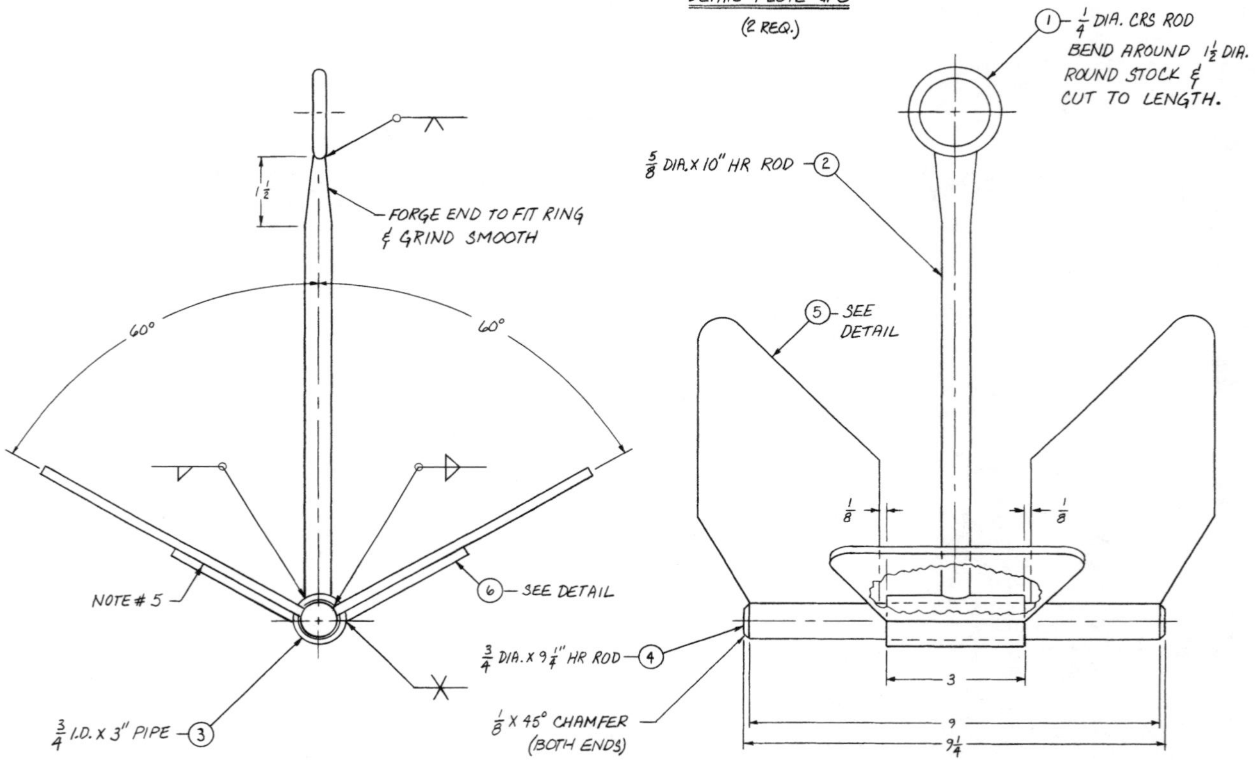
1 1/2
FORGE END TO FIT RING & GRIND SMOOTH
60°
60°
NOTE # 5
6 — SEE DETAIL
3/4 I.D. X 3" PIPE — 3
1 — 1/4 DIA. CRS ROD BEND AROUND 1 1/2 DIA. ROUND STOCK & CUT TO LENGTH.
5/8 DIA. X 10" HR ROD — 2
5 — SEE DETAIL
1/8
1/8
3/4 DIA. X 9 1/4" HR ROD — 4
1/8 X 45° CHAMFER (BOTH ENDS)
3
9
9 1/4

ASSEMBLY SEQUENCE:

1. WELD RING #1 TO SHANK # 2.
2. WELD SHANK # 2 TO PIVOT #3.
3. WELD ONE FLUTE #5 TO SWIVEL ARM # 4.
4. SLIDE SWIVEL ARM THROUGH PIVOT & WELD 2ND FLUTE IN PLACE. (ALLOW $\frac{1}{8}$ CLEARANCE)
5. PLACE FLUTES AT 60° TO ONE SIDE OF SHANK & POSITION CROWN PLATE #6 PARALLEL TO FLUTES. WELD IN PLACE.
6. REPEAT STEP #5 ON OPPOSITE SIDE.

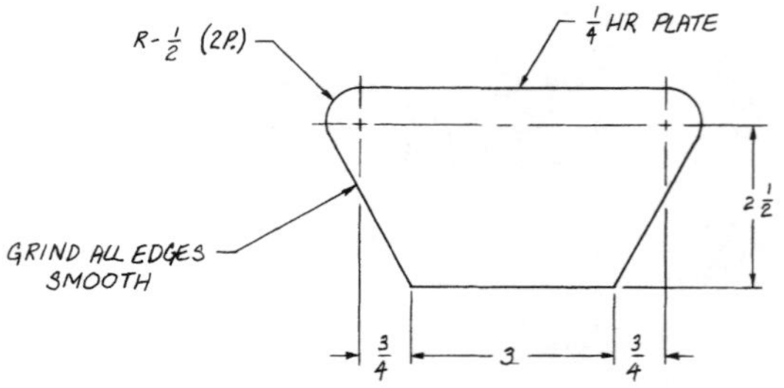
R - 1/2 (2 P.)
1/4 HR PLATE
GRIND ALL EDGES SMOOTH
2 1/2
3/4
3
3/4

DETAIL CROWN #6
(2 REQ.)

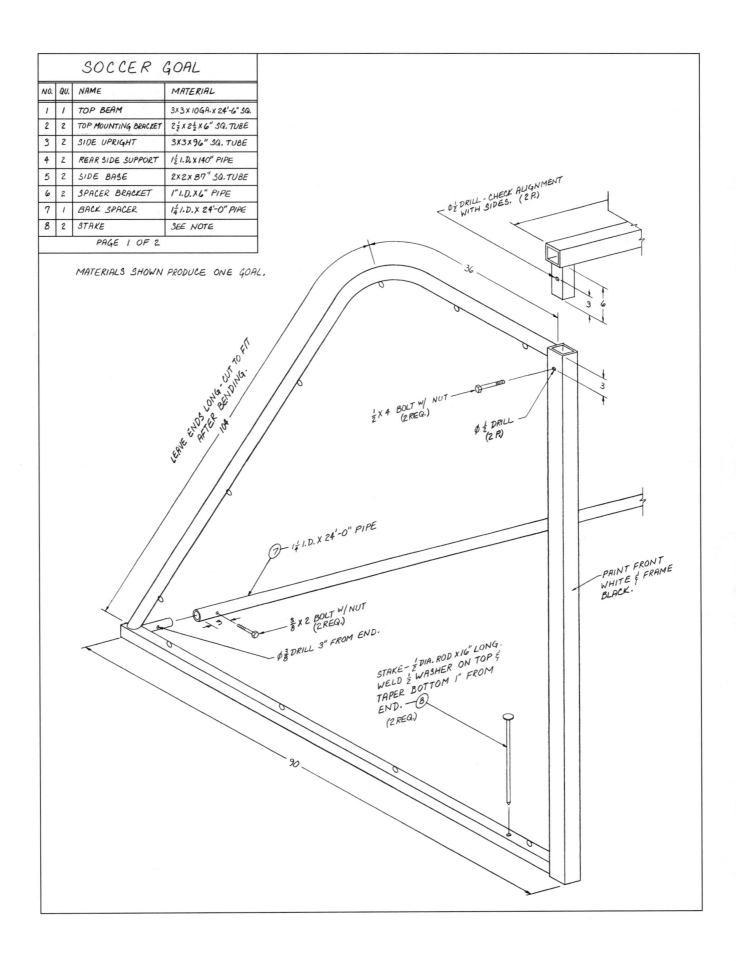

NO.	QU.	NAME	MATERIAL
1	1	TOP BEAM	3x3x10GA. x 24'-6" SQ.
2	2	TOP MOUNTING BRACKET	2½ x 2½ x 6" SQ. TUBE
3	2	SIDE UPRIGHT	3x3x96" SQ. TUBE
4	2	REAR SIDE SUPPORT	1½ I.D. X 140" PIPE
5	2	SIDE BASE	2x2x87" SQ. TUBE
6	2	SPACER BRACKET	1" I.D. X 6" PIPE
7	1	BACK SPACER	1¼ I.D. X 24'-0" PIPE
8	2	STAKE	SEE NOTE

SOCCER GOAL

PAGE 1 OF 2

MATERIALS SHOWN PRODUCE ONE GOAL.

Φ ½ DRILL - CHECK ALIGNMENT WITH SIDES. (2 PL.)

36

3   6

LEAVE ENDS LONG - CUT TO FIT AFTER BENDING.

104

½ X 4 BOLT W/ NUT (2 REQ.)

Φ ½ DRILL (2 PL.)

3

7   1¼ I.D. X 24'-0" PIPE

3

⅜ X 2 BOLT W/ NUT (2 REQ.)

Φ ⅜ DRILL 3" FROM END.

STAKE - ½ DIA. ROD X16" LONG. WELD ½ WASHER ON TOP & TAPER BOTTOM 1" FROM END. — 8 (2 REQ.)

PAINT FRONT WHITE & FRAME BLACK.

90

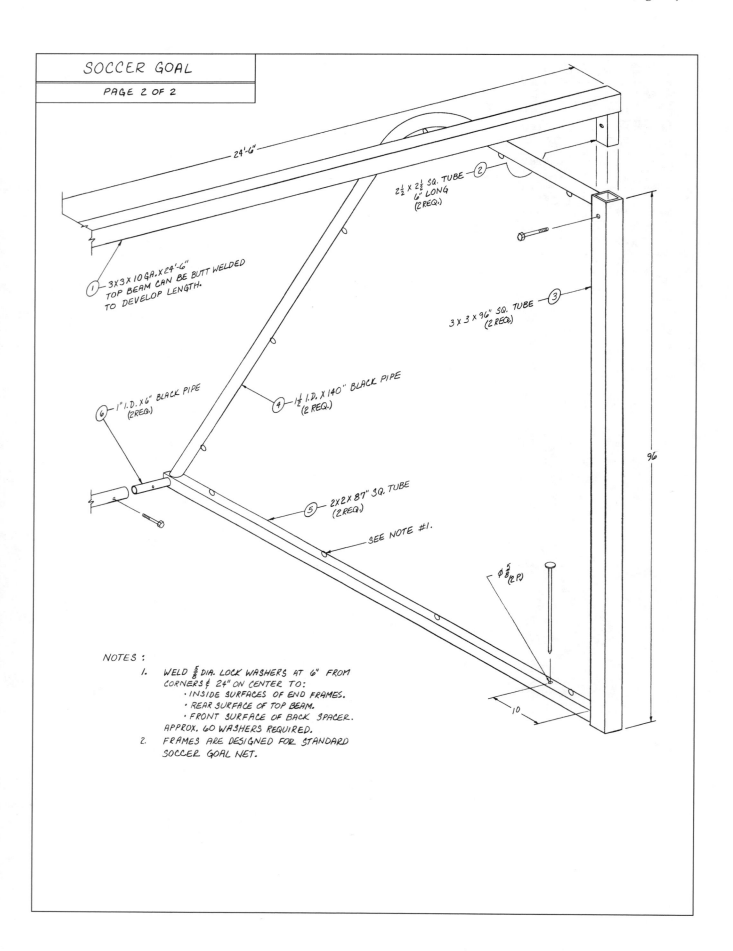

SOCCER GOAL

PAGE 2 OF 2

24'-6"

2½ X 2½ SQ. TUBE
6" LONG
(2 REQ.)

① 3X3 X 10 GA. X 24'-6"
TOP BEAM CAN BE BUTT WELDED
TO DEVELOP LENGTH.

3 X 3 X 96" SQ. TUBE
(2 REQ.)

96

⑥ 1" I.D. X 6" BLACK PIPE
(2 REQ.)

④ 1½ I.D. X 140" BLACK PIPE
(2 REQ.)

⑤ 2X2 X 87" SQ. TUBE
(2 REQ.)

SEE NOTE #1.

$\phi \frac{5}{8}$ (2 P.)

10

NOTES :
1. WELD $\frac{5}{8}$ DIA. LOCK WASHERS AT 6" FROM
    CORNERS & 24" ON CENTER TO:
    · INSIDE SURFACES OF END FRAMES.
    · REAR SURFACE OF TOP BEAM.
    · FRONT SURFACE OF BACK SPACER.
    APPROX. 60 WASHERS REQUIRED.
2. FRAMES ARE DESIGNED FOR STANDARD
    SOCCER GOAL NET.

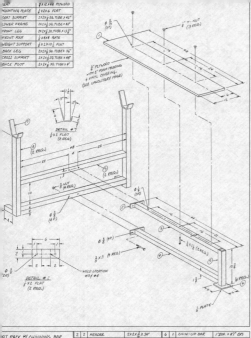

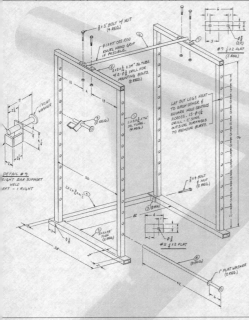

Gym Equipment

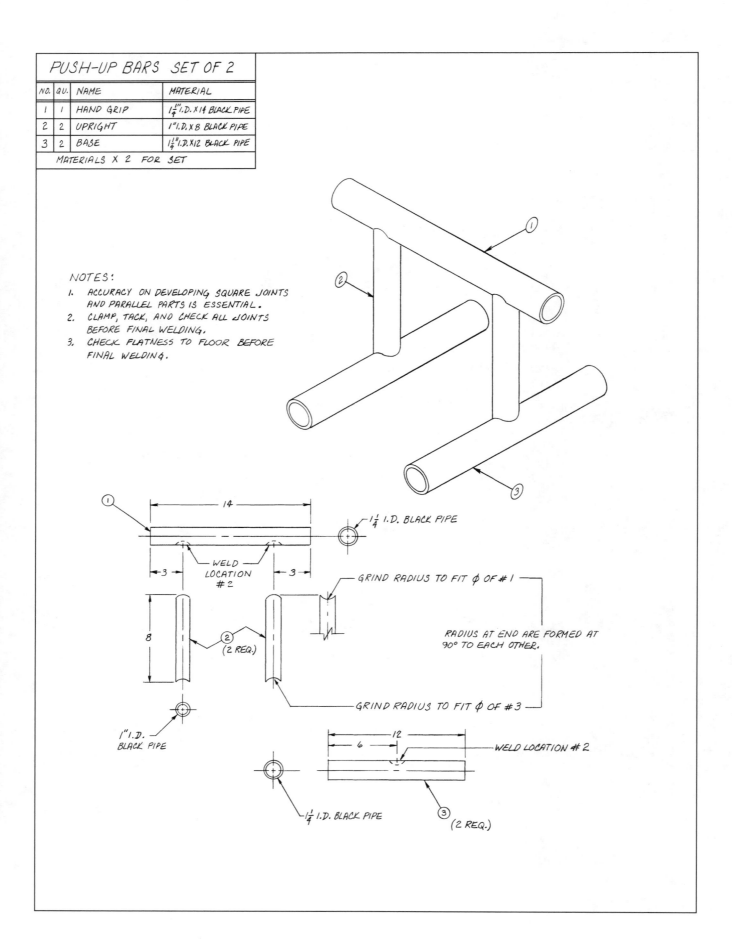

PUSH-UP BARS SET OF 2

NO.	QU.	NAME	MATERIAL
1	1	HAND GRIP	$1\frac{1}{4}''$ I.D. X 14 BLACK PIPE
2	2	UPRIGHT	$1''$ I.D. X 8 BLACK PIPE
3	2	BASE	$1\frac{1}{4}''$ I.D. X 12 BLACK PIPE

MATERIALS X 2 FOR SET

NOTES:

1. ACCURACY ON DEVELOPING SQUARE JOINTS AND PARALLEL PARTS IS ESSENTIAL.
2. CLAMP, TACK, AND CHECK ALL JOINTS BEFORE FINAL WELDING.
3. CHECK FLATNESS TO FLOOR BEFORE FINAL WELDING.

$1\frac{1}{4}$ I.D. BLACK PIPE

14

3   3

WELD LOCATION #2

GRIND RADIUS TO FIT ∅ OF #1

RADIUS AT END ARE FORMED AT 90° TO EACH OTHER.

8

2 (2 REQ.)

GRIND RADIUS TO FIT ∅ OF #3

1" I.D. BLACK PIPE

12

6

WELD LOCATION #2

$1\frac{1}{4}$ I.D. BLACK PIPE

3 (2 REQ.)

NO.	QU.	NAME	MATERIAL
1	1	SEAT	$\frac{3}{4}$ X 12 X 50 PLYWOOD
2	1	SEAT SUPPORT	2 X 2 X $\frac{1}{8}$ SQ. TUBE X 44"
3	2	LEG	2 X 2 X $\frac{1}{8}$ SQ. TUBE X 10"
4	2	BASE	2 X 2 X $\frac{1}{8}$ SQ. TUBE X 15"

BUTTERFLY BENCH

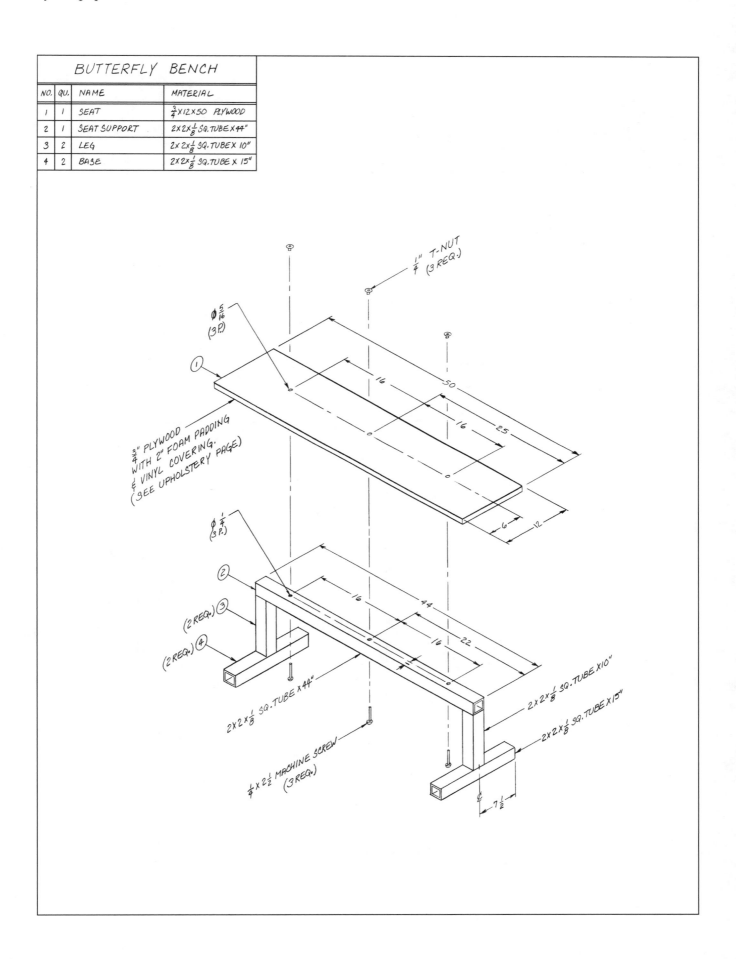

$\frac{1}{4}$" T-NUT (3 REQ.)

$\phi \frac{5}{16}$ (3 P.)

$\frac{3}{4}$" PLYWOOD WITH 2" FOAM PADDING & VINYL COVERING. (SEE UPHOLSTERY PAGE)

$\phi \frac{1}{4}$ (3 P.)

(2 REQ.) 3

(2 REQ.) 4

2 X 2 X $\frac{1}{8}$ SQ. TUBE X 44"

$\frac{1}{4}$ X 2 $\frac{1}{2}$ MACHINE SCREW (3 REQ.)

2 X 2 X $\frac{1}{8}$ SQ. TUBE X 10"

2 X 2 X $\frac{1}{8}$ SQ. TUBE X 15"

7 $\frac{1}{2}$

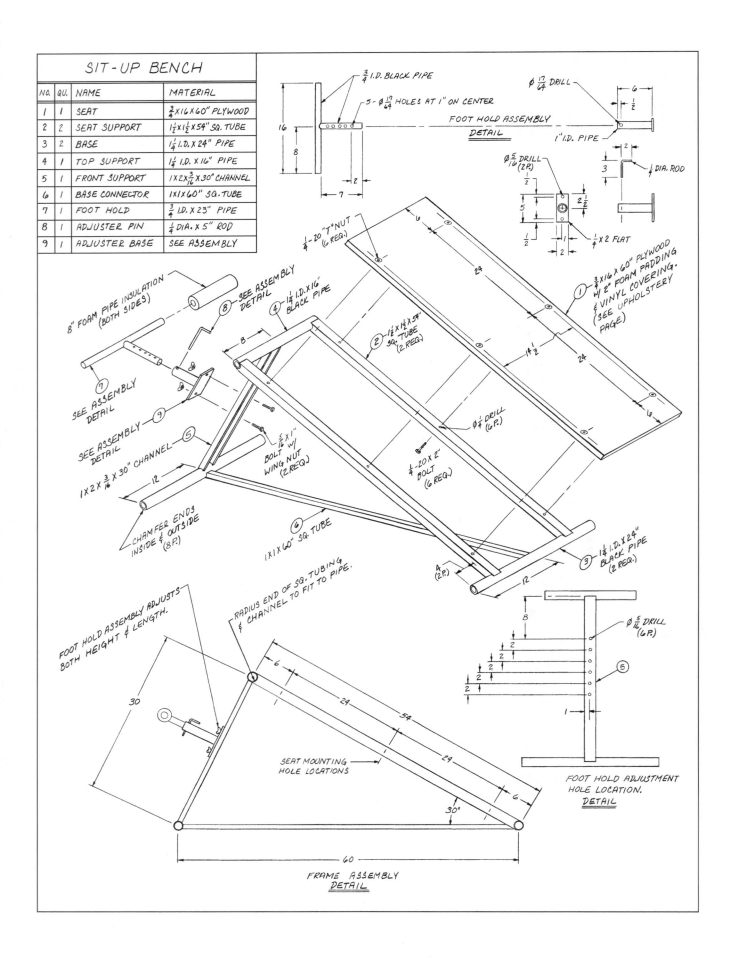

SIT-UP BENCH

NO.	QU.	NAME	MATERIAL
1	1	SEAT	¾ X 16 X 60" PLYWOOD
2	2	SEAT SUPPORT	1½ X 1½ X 54" SQ. TUBE
3	2	BASE	1¼ I.D. X 24" PIPE
4	1	TOP SUPPORT	1¼ I.D. X 16" PIPE
5	1	FRONT SUPPORT	1 X 2 X 3/16 X 30" CHANNEL
6	1	BASE CONNECTOR	1 X 1 X 60" SQ. TUBE
7	1	FOOT HOLD	¾ I.D. X 23" PIPE
8	1	ADJUSTER PIN	¼ DIA. X 5" ROD
9	1	ADJUSTER BASE	SEE ASSEMBLY

¾ I.D. BLACK PIPE

5 - Ø 17/64 HOLES AT 1" ON CENTER

FOOT HOLD ASSEMBLY
DETAIL

Ø 17/64 DRILL

1" I.D. PIPE

Ø 5/16 DRILL (2 P.)

¼ X 2 FLAT

¼ DIA. ROD

¼ - 20 "T" NUT (6 REQ.)

¾ X 16 X 60" PLYWOOD w/ 2" FOAM PADDING & VINYL COVERING. (SEE UPHOLSTERY PAGE)

8" FOAM PIPE INSULATION (BOTH SIDES)

SEE ASSEMBLY DETAIL

4 - 1¼ I.D. X 16" BLACK PIPE

2 - 1½ X 1½ X 54" SQ. TUBE (2 REQ.)

SEE ASSEMBLY DETAIL

SEE ASSEMBLY DETAIL

9

1 X 2 X 3/16 X 30" CHANNEL

5

5/16 X 1" BOLT w/ WING NUT (2 REQ.)

Ø ¼ DRILL (6 P.)

¼ - 20 X 2" BOLT (6 REQ.)

CHAMFER ENDS INSIDE & OUTSIDE (8 P.)

6

1 X 1 X 60" SQ. TUBE

A (2 P.)

3 - 1¼ I.D. X 24" BLACK PIPE (2 REQ.)

FOOT HOLD ASSEMBLY ADJUSTS BOTH HEIGHT & LENGTH.

RADIUS END OF SQ. TUBING & CHANNEL TO FIT TO PIPE.

Ø 5/16 DRILL (6 P.)

5

SEAT MOUNTING HOLE LOCATIONS

FOOT HOLD ADJUSTMENT HOLE LOCATION.
DETAIL

30°

60

FRAME ASSEMBLY
DETAIL

CURLING BENCH				NO.	QU.	NAME	MATERIAL
				3	2	HEIGHT ADJUSTER	ASSEMBLY
				4	1	WEIGHT REST	ASSEMBLY
NO.	QU.	NAME	MATERIAL	5	1	BODY SUPPORT	ASSEMBLY
1	1	BASE	ASSEMBLY	6	2	SUPPORT BOARD	¾ X 12 X 22 PLYWOOD
2	1	SEAT SUPPORT	ASSEMBLY	7	1	SEAT BOARD	¾ X 8 X 8 PLYWOOD

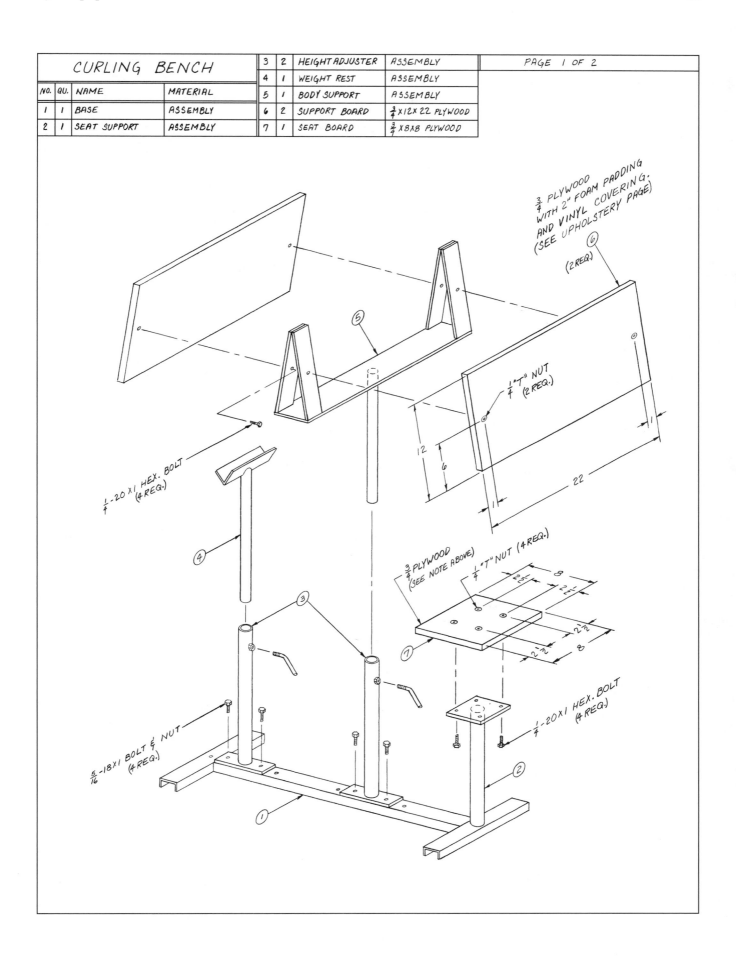

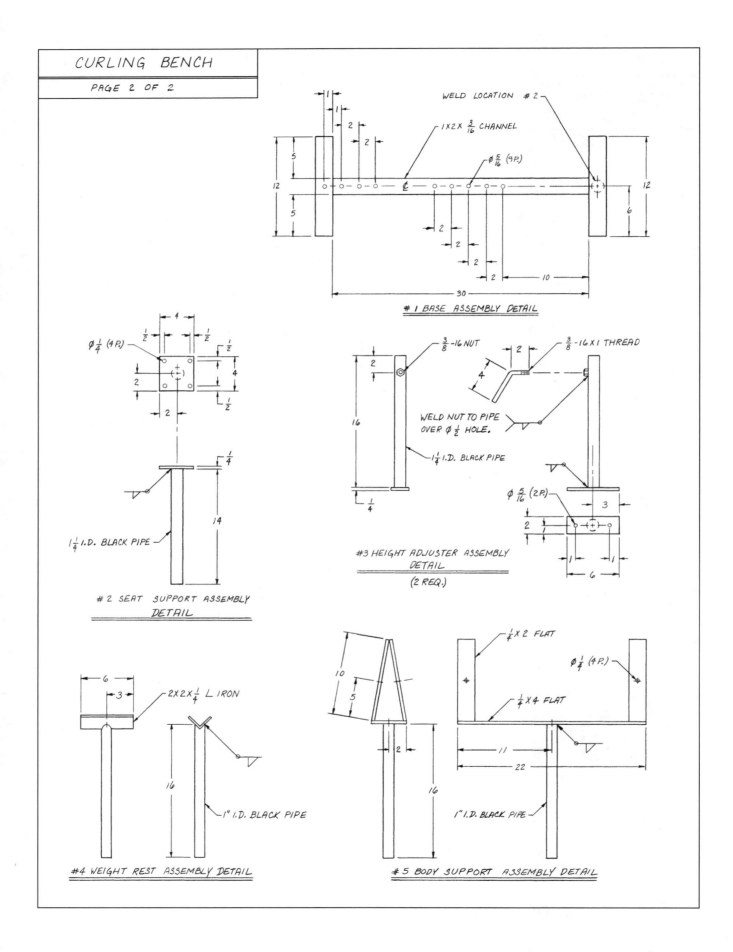

CURLING BENCH

WELD LOCATION #2

1X2X $\frac{3}{16}$ CHANNEL

$\phi \frac{5}{16}$ (9 P.)

1 BASE ASSEMBLY DETAIL

$\phi \frac{1}{4}$ (4 P.)

2 SEAT SUPPORT ASSEMBLY DETAIL

$1\frac{1}{4}$ I.D. BLACK PIPE

$\frac{3}{8}$ -16 NUT

$\frac{3}{8}$ -16 X 1 THREAD

WELD NUT TO PIPE OVER $\phi \frac{1}{2}$ HOLE.

$1\frac{1}{4}$ I.D. BLACK PIPE

$\phi \frac{5}{16}$ (2 P.)

#3 HEIGHT ADJUSTER ASSEMBLY DETAIL

(2 REQ.)

2X2X $\frac{1}{4}$ L IRON

1" I.D. BLACK PIPE

#4 WEIGHT REST ASSEMBLY DETAIL

$\frac{1}{4}$ X 2 FLAT

$\phi \frac{1}{4}$ (4 P.)

$\frac{1}{4}$ X 4 FLAT

1" I.D. BLACK PIPE

5 BODY SUPPORT ASSEMBLY DETAIL

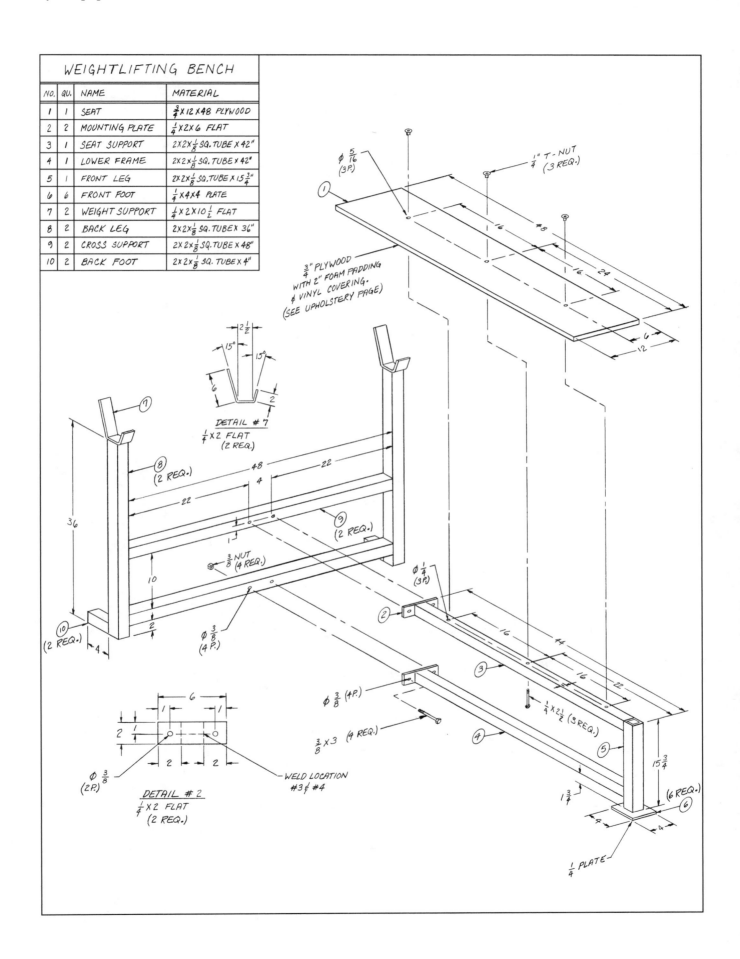

WEIGHTLIFTING BENCH

NO.	QU.	NAME	MATERIAL
1	1	SEAT	$\frac{3}{4}$ X 12 X 48 PLYWOOD
2	2	MOUNTING PLATE	$\frac{1}{4}$ X 2 X 6 FLAT
3	1	SEAT SUPPORT	2 X 2 X $\frac{1}{8}$ SQ. TUBE X 42"
4	1	LOWER FRAME	2 X 2 X $\frac{1}{8}$ SQ. TUBE X 42"
5	1	FRONT LEG	2 X 2 X $\frac{1}{8}$ SQ. TUBE X 15 $\frac{3}{4}$"
6	6	FRONT FOOT	$\frac{1}{4}$ X 4 X 4 PLATE
7	2	WEIGHT SUPPORT	$\frac{1}{4}$ X 2 X 10 $\frac{1}{2}$ FLAT
8	2	BACK LEG	2 X 2 X $\frac{1}{8}$ SQ. TUBE X 36"
9	2	CROSS SUPPORT	2 X 2 X $\frac{1}{8}$ SQ. TUBE X 48"
10	2	BACK FOOT	2 X 2 X $\frac{1}{8}$ SQ. TUBE X 4"

$\phi \frac{5}{16}$ (3 P.)

1" T-NUT (3 REQ.)

$\frac{3}{4}$" PLYWOOD WITH 2" FOAM PADDING & VINYL COVERING. (SEE UPHOLSTERY PAGE)

DETAIL # 7
$\frac{1}{4}$ X 2 FLAT
(2 REQ.)

(8) (2 REQ.)

(9) (2 REQ.)

$\frac{3}{8}$ NUT (4 REQ.)

(10) (2 REQ.)

$\phi \frac{3}{8}$ (4 P.)

$\phi \frac{1}{4}$ (3 P.)

$\frac{1}{4}$ X 2 $\frac{1}{2}$ (3 REQ.)

$\phi \frac{3}{8}$ (4 P.)

$\frac{3}{8}$ X 3 (4 REQ.)

$\phi \frac{3}{8}$ (2 P.)

DETAIL # 2
$\frac{1}{4}$ X 2 FLAT
(2 REQ.)

WELD LOCATION #3 & #4

$15 \frac{3}{4}$

$1 \frac{3}{4}$

(6 REQ.)

$\frac{1}{4}$ PLATE

INCLINED BENCH

NO.	QU.	NAME	MATERIAL
1	2	WEIGHT SUPPORT	$\frac{1}{4} \times 2 \times 12\frac{1}{2}$"
2	2	EXTENDER	$1\frac{1}{2} \times 1\frac{1}{2} \times \frac{1}{8} \times 24$"
3	3	PIN	$\phi 1$" $\times 3\frac{1}{2}$ CRS
4	3	QUICK CLIP	HARDWARE
5	2	UPRIGHT	$2 \times 2 \times \frac{3}{16} \times 36$"
6	2	CROSS MEMBER	$2 \times 2 \times \frac{3}{16} \times 44$"
7	2	PIVOT	$\frac{1}{4} \times 2 \times 4\frac{1}{2}$"
8	1	REAR SUPPORT	$2 \times 2 \times \frac{3}{16} \times 16$"
9	1	FRONT SUPPORT	$2 \times 2 \times \frac{3}{16} \times 18$"
10	1	LEG	$2 \times 2 \times \frac{3}{16} \times 11\frac{3}{4}$"
11	1	FOOT	$\frac{1}{4} \times 4 \times 4$
12	3	BOLT & NUT	$\frac{1}{2}$-13 NC $\times 3$"
13	2	PIVOT	$\frac{1}{4} \times 2 \times 4\frac{1}{2}$"
14	1	SEAT EXTENDER	$1\frac{1}{2} \times 1\frac{1}{2} \times \frac{1}{8} \times 24$"
15	1	SEAT UPRIGHT	$2 \times 2 \times \frac{3}{16} \times 20$"
16	1	BACK SUPPORT	$1\frac{1}{2} \times 3 \times 36$"
17	1	SEAT SUPPORT	$1\frac{1}{2} \times 3 \times 12$"
18	2	PIVOT	$\frac{1}{4} \times 2 \times 4\frac{1}{2}$"
19	1	SEAT BACK	$\frac{3}{4} \times 10$" $\times 40$"
20	1	SEAT BOTTOM	$\frac{3}{4} \times 10$" $\times 12$"

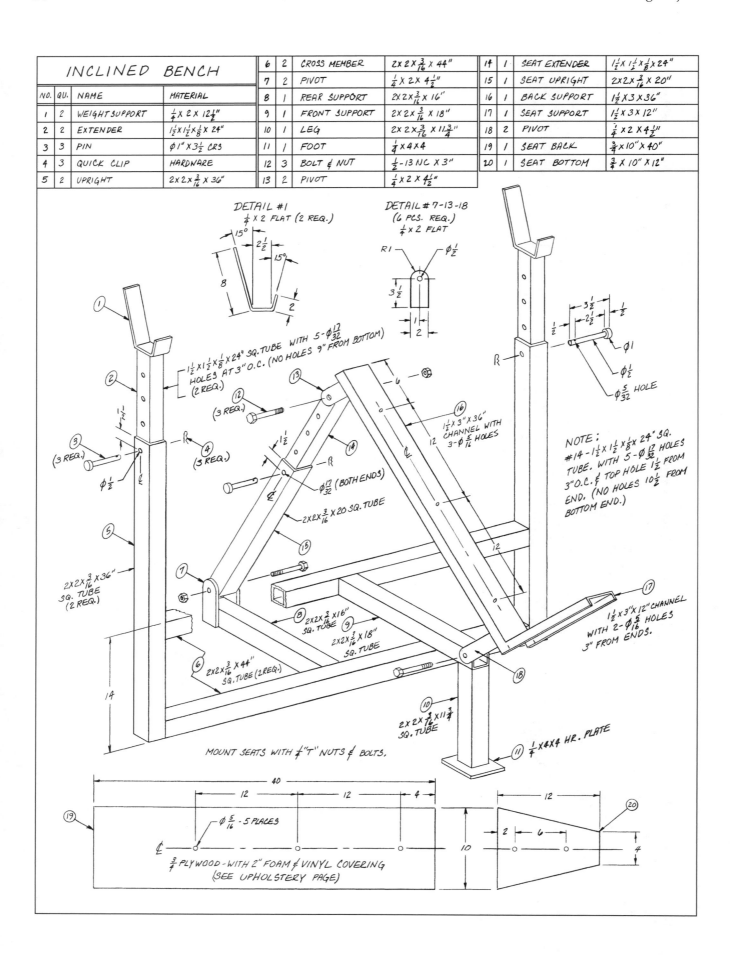

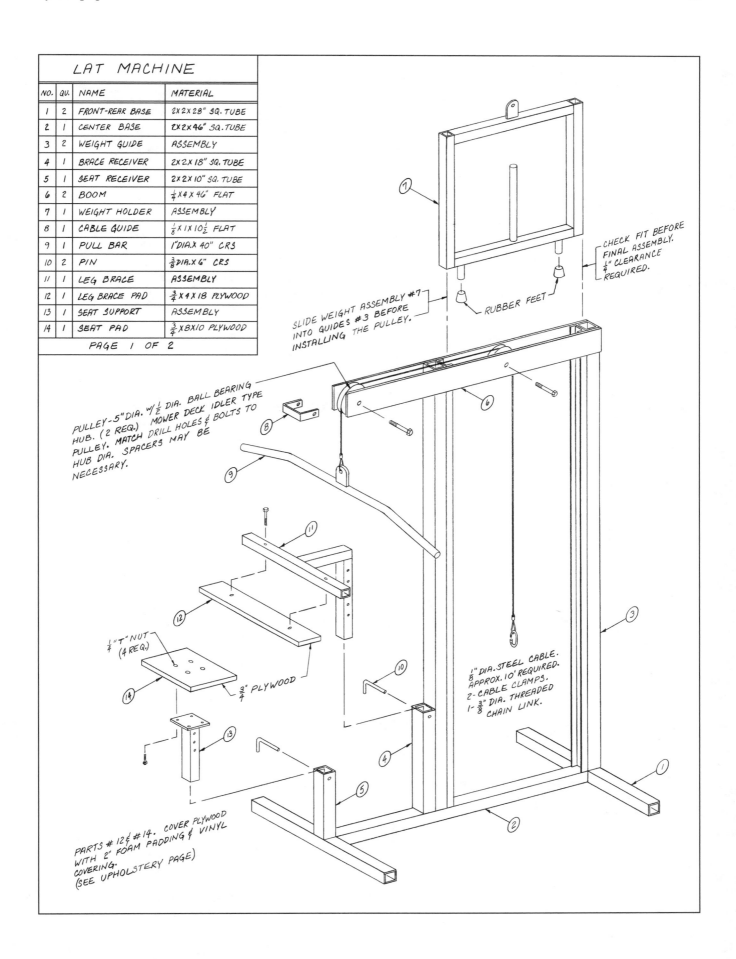

LAT MACHINE

NO.	QU.	NAME	MATERIAL
1	2	FRONT-REAR BASE	2×2×28" SQ. TUBE
2	1	CENTER BASE	2×2×46" SQ. TUBE
3	2	WEIGHT GUIDE	ASSEMBLY
4	1	BRACE RECEIVER	2×2×18" SQ. TUBE
5	1	SEAT RECEIVER	2×2×10" SQ. TUBE
6	2	BOOM	$\frac{1}{4}$×4×46" FLAT
7	1	WEIGHT HOLDER	ASSEMBLY
8	1	CABLE GUIDE	$\frac{1}{8}$×1×10$\frac{1}{2}$ FLAT
9	1	PULL BAR	1"DIA.×40" CRS
10	2	PIN	$\frac{3}{8}$DIA.×6" CRS
11	1	LEG BRACE	ASSEMBLY
12	1	LEG BRACE PAD	$\frac{3}{4}$×4×18 PLYWOOD
13	1	SEAT SUPPORT	ASSEMBLY
14	1	SEAT PAD	$\frac{3}{4}$×8×10 PLYWOOD

PAGE 1 OF 2

CHECK FIT BEFORE FINAL ASSEMBLY. $\frac{1}{4}$" CLEARANCE REQUIRED.

RUBBER FEET

SLIDE WEIGHT ASSEMBLY #7 INTO GUIDES #3 BEFORE INSTALLING THE PULLEY.

PULLEY-5"DIA. w/ $\frac{1}{2}$ DIA. BALL BEARING HUB. (2 REQ.) MOWER DECK IDLER TYPE PULLEY. MATCH DRILL HOLES & BOLTS TO HUB DIA. SPACERS MAY BE NECESSARY.

$\frac{1}{4}$ "T" NUT (4 REQ.)

$\frac{3}{4}$" PLYWOOD

$\frac{1}{8}$" DIA. STEEL CABLE. APPROX. 10' REQUIRED.
2 - CABLE CLAMPS.
1 - $\frac{3}{8}$" DIA. THREADED CHAIN LINK.

PARTS # 12 & #14. COVER PLYWOOD WITH 2" FOAM PADDING & VINYL COVERING. (SEE UPHOLSTERY PAGE)

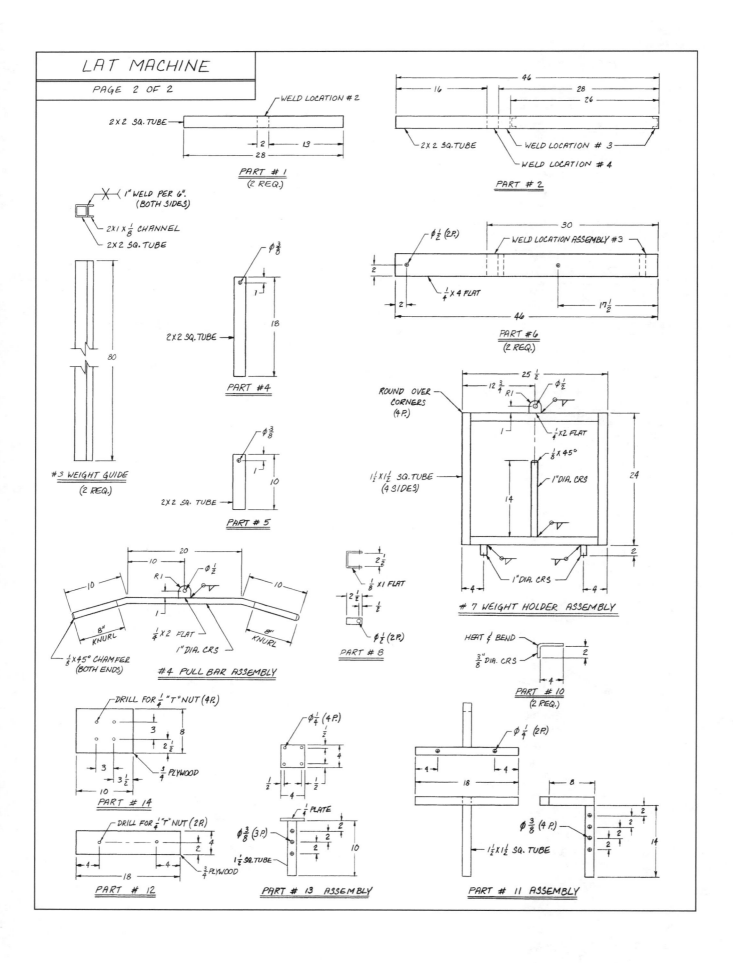

LAT MACHINE
PAGE 2 OF 2

WELD LOCATION #2
2X2 SQ. TUBE
2 · 13 · 28
PART #1
(2 REQ.)

46 · 16 · 28 · 26
2X2 SQ. TUBE · WELD LOCATION #3 · WELD LOCATION #4
PART #2

1" WELD PER 6". (BOTH SIDES)
2X1X⅛ CHANNEL
2X2 SQ. TUBE

φ⅜
1
18
2X2 SQ. TUBE
PART #4

φ½ (2P.)
2
2
WELD LOCATION ASSEMBLY #3
¼ X 4 FLAT
30 · 17½ · 46
PART #6
(2 REQ.)

80
#3 WEIGHT GUIDE
(2 REQ.)

φ⅜
1
10
2X2 SQ. TUBE
PART #5

ROUND OVER CORNERS (4 P.)
25½ · 12¾ · R1 · φ½
1 · ¼ X2 FLAT
1½ X1½ SQ. TUBE (4 SIDES)
⅛ X 45°
1"DIA. CRS
14
24
2
#7 WEIGHT HOLDER ASSEMBLY
4 · 1"DIA. CRS · 4

20 · 10 · 10
R1 · φ½
1 · 10
8" KNURL · 8" KNURL
¼ X2 FLAT · 1"DIA. CRS
⅛ X45° CHAMFER (BOTH ENDS)
#4 PULL BAR ASSEMBLY

2½ · ⅛ X1 FLAT
2½ · ½
φ½ (2P.)
PART #8

HEAT & BEND
⅜" DIA. CRS
2 · 4
PART #10
(2 REQ.)

DRILL FOR ¼" "T" NUT (4P.)
3 · 8 · 2½
3 · 3½ · ¼ PLYWOOD
10
PART #14

φ¼ (4P.)
½
4
½ · 4 · ½
¼ PLATE
φ⅜ (3P.)
2 · 2 · 2
10
1½ SQ. TUBE
PART #13 ASSEMBLY

φ¼ (2P.)
4 · 4
18
1½ X1½ SQ. TUBE
8 · 2 · 2 · 2 · 2
φ⅜ (4P.)
14
PART #11 ASSEMBLY

DRILL FOR ¼" "T" NUT (2P.)
4 · 2 · 2
4 · 4
18 · ¾ PLYWOOD
PART #12

NO	QU.	NAME	MATERIAL
		SQUAT RACK w/ CHINNING BAR	
1	4	LEG	2X2X$\frac{3}{16}$X76"
2	2	HEADER	2X2X$\frac{3}{16}$X34"
3	2	BASE	2X3X38"
4	1	REAR SUPPORT	2X2X$\frac{3}{16}$X41$\frac{1}{2}$"
5	2	SUPPORT BRACKETS	$\frac{1}{4}$X2X4 FLAT
6	1	CHIN-UP BAR	1"DIA.X47" CRS
7	2	BAR BRACKET	$\frac{1}{4}$X2X6 FLAT
8	2	SAFETY BAR	ASSEMBLY
9	2	WEIGHT BAR SUPT.	ASSEMBLY

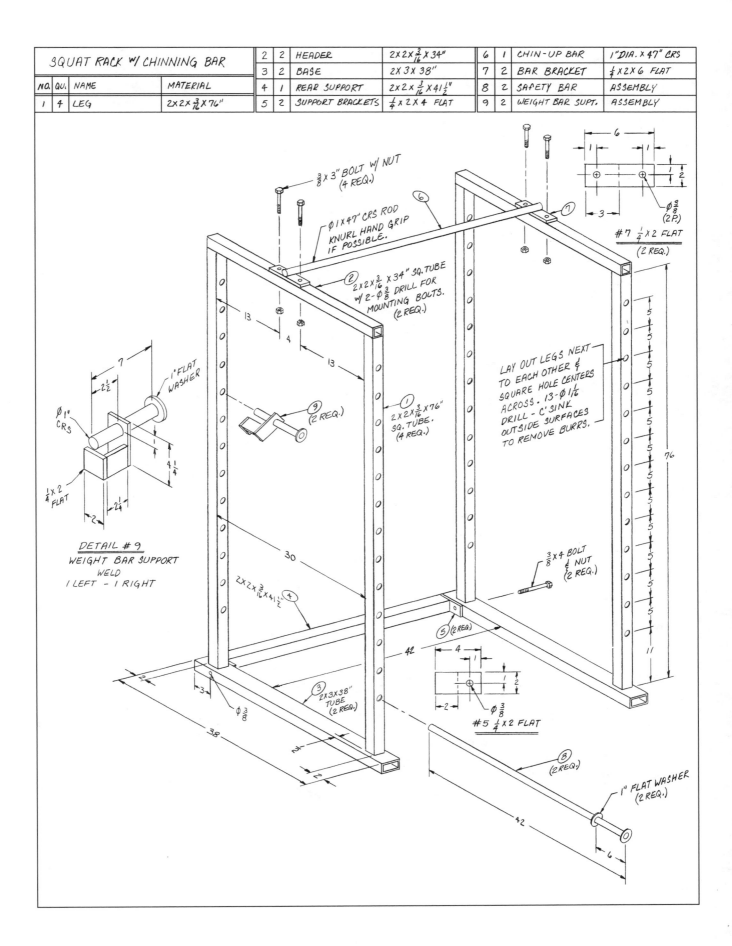

$\frac{3}{8}$ X 3" BOLT W/ NUT (4 REQ.)

Ø 1 X 47" CRS ROD KNURL HAND GRIP IF POSSIBLE.

2 X 2 X $\frac{3}{16}$ X 34" SQ. TUBE w/ 2-Ø$\frac{3}{8}$ DRILL FOR MOUNTING BOLTS. (2 REQ.)

6

#7 $\frac{1}{4}$ X 2 FLAT (2 REQ.)

Ø$\frac{3}{8}$ (2 P.)

7

1" FLAT WASHER

Ø 1" CRS

$\frac{1}{4}$ X 2 FLAT

DETAIL #9
WEIGHT BAR SUPPORT
WELD
1 LEFT - 1 RIGHT

9 (2 REQ.)

1
2 X 2 X $\frac{3}{16}$ X 76" SQ. TUBE. (4 REQ.)

LAY OUT LEGS NEXT TO EACH OTHER & SQUARE HOLE CENTERS ACROSS. 13-Ø 1/16 DRILL - C'SINK OUTSIDE SURFACES TO REMOVE BURRS.

$\frac{3}{8}$ X 4 BOLT & NUT (2 REQ.)

76

4
2 X 2 X $\frac{3}{16}$ X 41$\frac{1}{2}$

30

3
2X3X38" TUBE (2 REQ.)

5 (2 REQ.)

4

Ø$\frac{3}{8}$

#5 $\frac{1}{4}$ X 2 FLAT

38

8 (2 REQ.)

1" FLAT WASHER (2 REQ.)

42

6

NO.	QU.	NAME	MATERIAL
		STAIR STEPPER	
1	1	HANDLE BAR	ASSEMBLY
2	1	COLUMN	$2\frac{1}{2} \times 2\frac{1}{2} \times \frac{1}{8} \times 48''$
3	1	RAM SUPPORT	$\frac{1}{2}$ I.D. PIPE $\times 10\frac{1}{2}''$
4	1	COLUMN BRACE	$\frac{1}{4} \times 2 \times 42''$
5	2	PIVOT ARM	ASSEMBLY

6	8	PIVOT BRACKET	$\frac{3}{8} \times 1\frac{1}{2} \times 2\frac{1}{4}''$
7	2	FOOT PAD	$\frac{3}{4} \times 5 \times 12$ PLYWOOD
8	1	PULLEY	SEE NOTE #1
9	1	CABLE	$\frac{1}{8}$ STEEL CABLE 36''
10	1	FRONT SUPPORT	$2\frac{1}{2} \times 2\frac{1}{2} \times \frac{1}{8} \times 14''$
11	1	CENTER SUPPORT	$2\frac{1}{2} \times 2\frac{1}{2} \times \frac{1}{8} \times 48''$
12	1	REAR SUPPORT	$2\frac{1}{2} \times 2\frac{1}{2} \times \frac{1}{8} \times 24''$
		PAGE 1 OF 2	

BICYCLE HAND GRIP
OPTIONAL
(2 REQ.)

$\frac{3}{8} \times 1\frac{1}{2}$ CARRIAGE
BOLT W/ NUT
(4 REQ.)

CAR SHOCK - CUT DUST COVERS
FROM ROD END. (2 REQ.)

$\frac{3}{8} \times 2\frac{1}{2}$ BOLT W/ NUT
(2 REQ.)

$\frac{3}{8} \times 1$ BOLT
W/ NUT
(2 REQ.)

$\frac{3}{8} \times 3\frac{1}{2}$ BOLT W/ NUT
(2 REQ.)

NOTES:
1. PART #8 - 4''DIA. GARAGE DOOR PULLEY.
2. PART #9 - $\frac{1}{8}$ DIA. STEEL CABLE W/ 2 CABLE
   CLAMPS. END OF LOOPS APPROX. 28''
   APART.

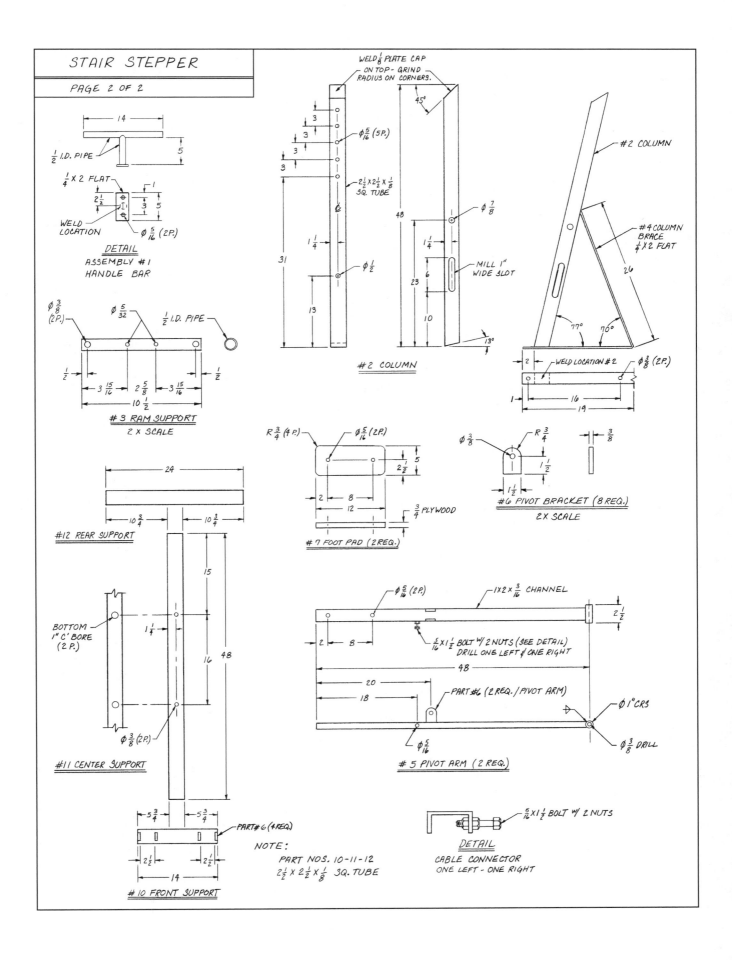

STAIR STEPPER

PAGE 2 OF 2

DETAIL
ASSEMBLY #1
HANDLE BAR

#3 RAM SUPPORT
2 X SCALE

#12 REAR SUPPORT

#11 CENTER SUPPORT

#2 COLUMN

#7 FOOT PAD (2 REQ.)

#6 PIVOT BRACKET (8 REQ.)
2X SCALE

#5 PIVOT ARM (2 REQ.)

#10 FRONT SUPPORT

NOTE:
PART NOS. 10-11-12
$2\frac{1}{2} \times 2\frac{1}{2} \times \frac{1}{8}$ SQ. TUBE

DETAIL
CABLE CONNECTOR
ONE LEFT - ONE RIGHT

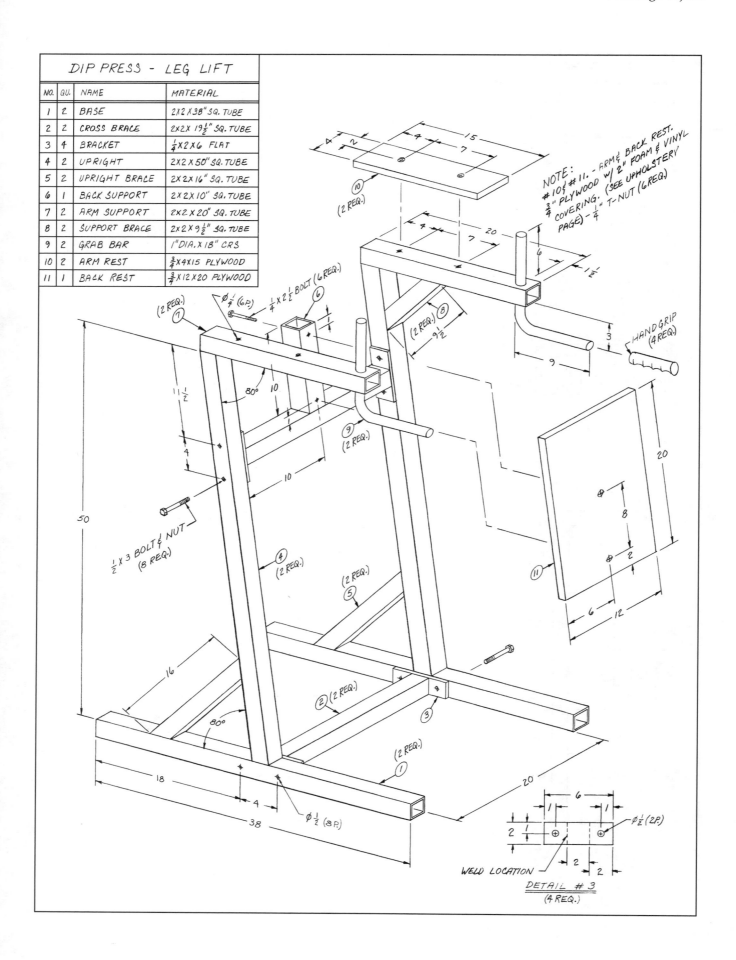

NO.	QU.	NAME	MATERIAL
1	2	BASE	2X2X38" SQ. TUBE
2	2	CROSS BRACE	2X2X19½" SQ. TUBE
3	4	BRACKET	¼X2X6 FLAT
4	2	UPRIGHT	2X2X50" SQ. TUBE
5	2	UPRIGHT BRACE	2X2X16" SQ. TUBE
6	1	BACK SUPPORT	2X2X10" SQ. TUBE
7	2	ARM SUPPORT	2X2X20" SQ. TUBE
8	2	SUPPORT BRACE	2X2X9½" SQ. TUBE
9	2	GRAB BAR	1"DIA.X18" CRS
10	2	ARM REST	¾X4X15 PLYWOOD
11	1	BACK REST	¾X12X20 PLYWOOD

DIP PRESS - LEG LIFT

NOTE:
#10 & #11. - ARM & BACK REST.
¾" PLYWOOD w/ 2" FOAM & VINYL
COVERING. (SEE UPHOLSTERY
PAGE) - ¼" T-NUT (6 REQ.)

HANDGRIP (4 REQ.)

WELD LOCATION

DETAIL # 3
(4 REQ.)

NO.	QU.	NAME	MATERIAL
1	2	WALL BRACKET	$\frac{1}{4}$ X 2 X 38 FLAT
2	2	BAR SUPPORT	$\frac{1}{2}$ I.D. X 45 PIPE
3	1	BAR	$\frac{3}{4}$ I.D. X 31 PIPE

CHIN - UP BAR

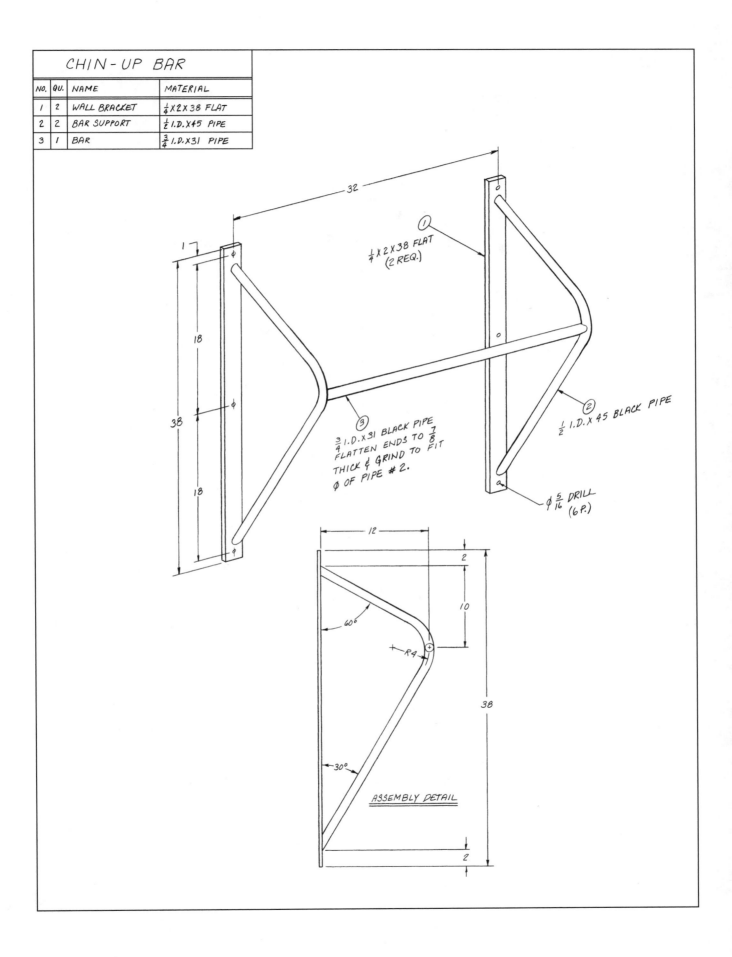

$\frac{1}{4}$ X 2 X 38 FLAT
(2 REQ.)

32

1

18

38

18

$\frac{3}{4}$ I.D. X 31 BLACK PIPE
FLATTEN ENDS TO $\frac{7}{8}$
THICK & GRIND TO FIT
ϕ OF PIPE #2.

$\frac{1}{2}$ I.D. X 45 BLACK PIPE

$\phi \frac{5}{16}$ DRILL
(6 P.)

12

2

10

60°

R4

38

30°

2

ASSEMBLY DETAIL

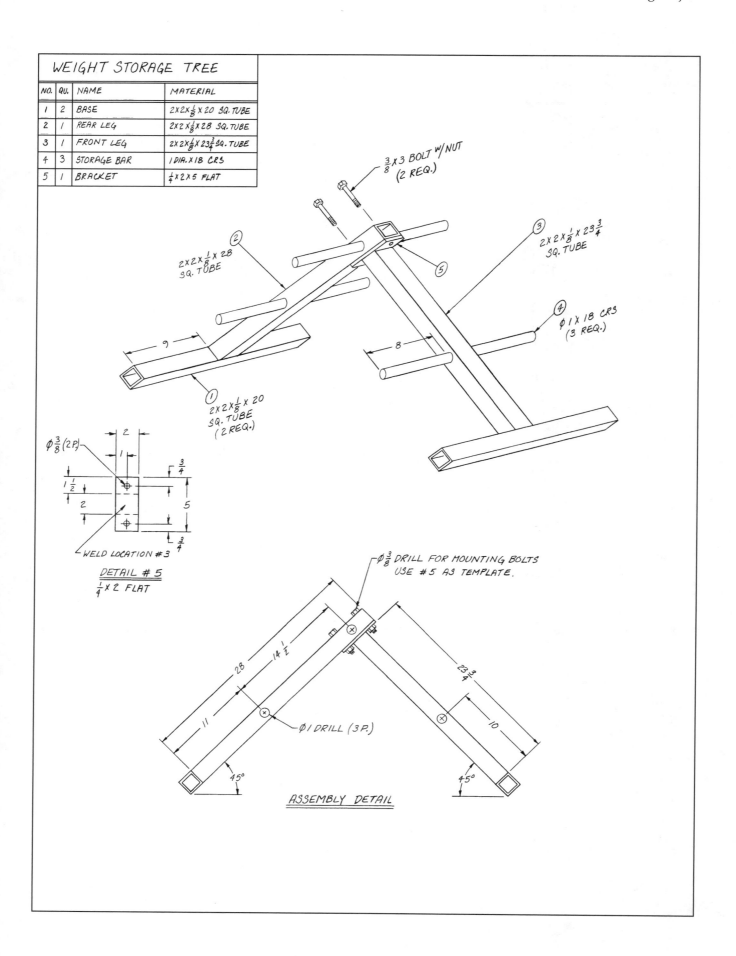

WEIGHT STORAGE TREE

NO.	QU.	NAME	MATERIAL
1	2	BASE	2x2x⅛ x 20 SQ. TUBE
2	1	REAR LEG	2x2x⅛ x28 SQ. TUBE
3	1	FRONT LEG	2x2x⅛ x 23¾ SQ. TUBE
4	3	STORAGE BAR	1 DIA. x 18 CRS
5	1	BRACKET	¼ x2 x 5 FLAT

⅜ x 3 BOLT w/ NUT (2 REQ.)

② 2x2x⅛ x 28 SQ. TUBE

③ 2x2x⅛ x 23¾ SQ. TUBE

⑤

④ Ø 1 x 18 CRS (3 REQ.)

9

8

① 2x2x⅛ x 20 SQ. TUBE (2 REQ.)

Ø⅜ (2P.)

2

1

1½

2

¾

5

¾

WELD LOCATION #3

DETAIL #5
¼ x 2 FLAT

Ø⅜ DRILL FOR MOUNTING BOLTS USE #5 AS TEMPLATE.

28

14½

11

Ø1 DRILL (3 P.)

23¾

10

45°

45°

ASSEMBLY DETAIL

DEAD LIFT BAR			
NO.	QU.	NAME	MATERIAL
1	2	WEIGHT BAR	1" DIA. CRS 14"
2	2	YOKE	1" DIA. CRS 42" APPROX.
3	2	HANDLE	1" DIA. CRS 9"

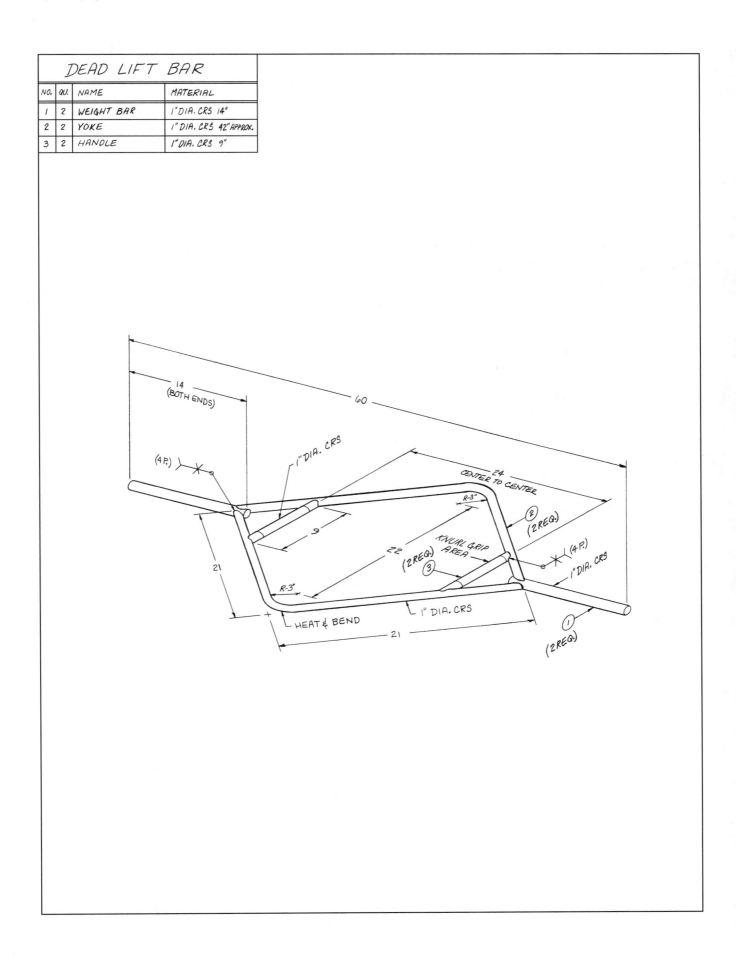

Shop
Equipment

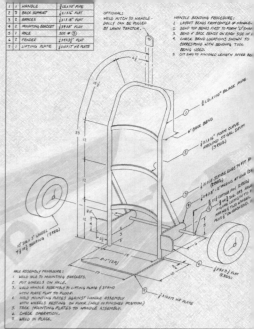

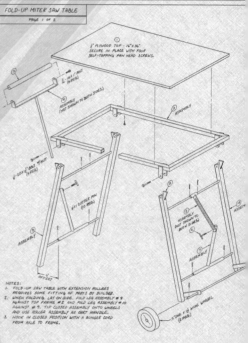

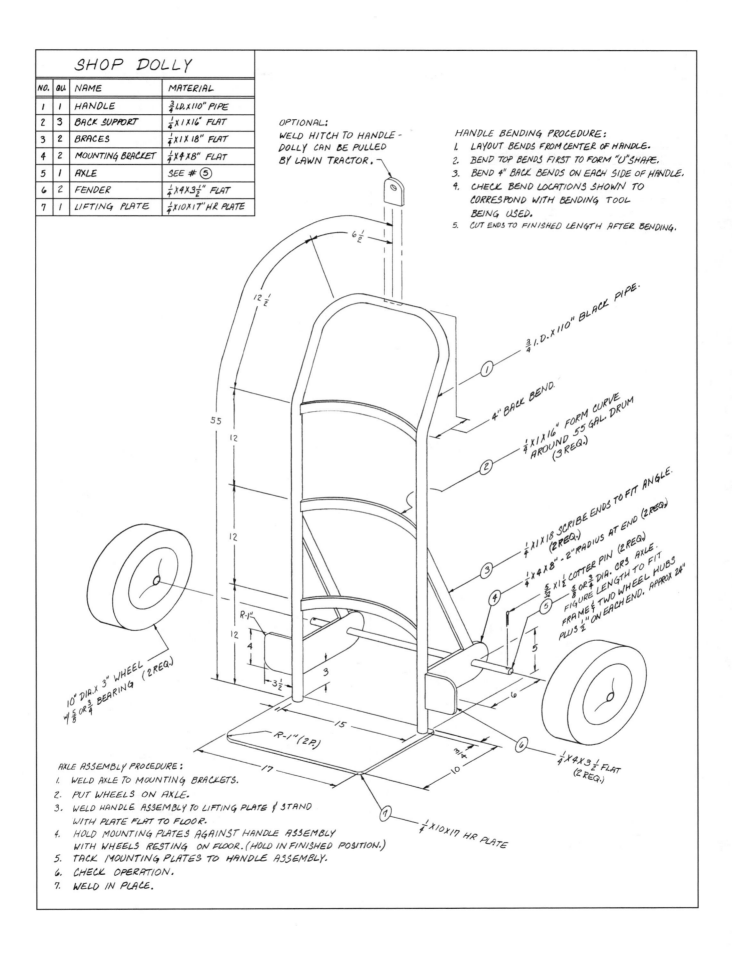

SHOP DOLLY

NO.	QU.	NAME	MATERIAL
1	1	HANDLE	$\frac{3}{4}$ I.D. X 110" PIPE
2	3	BACK SUPPORT	$\frac{1}{4}$ X 1 X 16" FLAT
3	2	BRACES	$\frac{1}{4}$ X 1 X 18" FLAT
4	2	MOUNTING BRACKET	$\frac{1}{4}$ X 4 X 8" FLAT
5	1	AXLE	SEE # ⑤
6	2	FENDER	$\frac{1}{4}$ X 4 X 3$\frac{1}{2}$" FLAT
7	1	LIFTING PLATE	$\frac{1}{4}$ X 10 X 17" HR PLATE

OPTIONAL:
WELD HITCH TO HANDLE -
DOLLY CAN BE PULLED
BY LAWN TRACTOR.

HANDLE BENDING PROCEDURE:
1. LAYOUT BENDS FROM CENTER OF HANDLE.
2. BEND TOP BENDS FIRST TO FORM "U" SHAPE.
3. BEND 4" BACK BENDS ON EACH SIDE OF HANDLE.
4. CHECK BEND LOCATIONS SHOWN TO
   CORRESPOND WITH BENDING TOOL
   BEING USED.
5. CUT ENDS TO FINISHED LENGTH AFTER BENDING.

$\frac{3}{4}$ I.D. X 110" BLACK PIPE.

4" BACK BEND.

$\frac{1}{4}$ X 1 X 16" FORM CURVE
AROUND 55 GAL. DRUM
(3 REQ.)

$\frac{1}{4}$ X 1 X 18 SCRIBE ENDS TO FIT ANGLE.
(2 REQ.)

$\frac{1}{4}$ X 4 X 8" - 2" RADIUS AT END (2 REQ.)

$\frac{5}{32}$ X 1$\frac{1}{2}$ COTTER PIN (2 REQ.)

$\frac{5}{8}$ OR $\frac{3}{4}$ DIA. CR3 AXLE.
FIGURE LENGTH TO FIT
FRAME & TWO WHEEL HUBS
PLUS $\frac{1}{4}$" ON EACH END. APPROX 24"

10" DIA. X 3" WHEEL
W/ $\frac{5}{8}$ OR $\frac{3}{4}$ BEARING (2 REQ.)

$\frac{1}{4}$ X 4 X 3$\frac{1}{2}$ FLAT
(2 REQ.)

$\frac{1}{4}$ X 10 X 17 HR PLATE

AXLE ASSEMBLY PROCEDURE:
1. WELD AXLE TO MOUNTING BRACKETS.
2. PUT WHEELS ON AXLE.
3. WELD HANDLE ASSEMBLY TO LIFTING PLATE & STAND
   WITH PLATE FLAT TO FLOOR.
4. HOLD MOUNTING PLATES AGAINST HANDLE ASSEMBLY
   WITH WHEELS RESTING ON FLOOR. (HOLD IN FINISHED POSITION.)
5. TACK MOUNTING PLATES TO HANDLE ASSEMBLY.
6. CHECK OPERATION.
7. WELD IN PLACE.

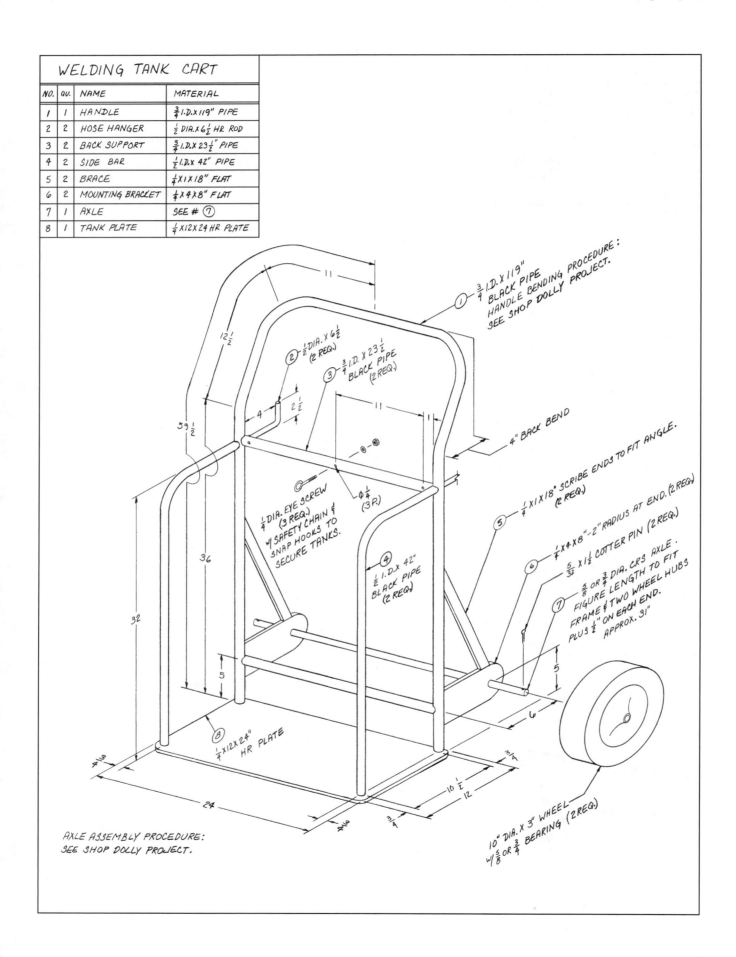

WELDING TANK CART

NO.	QU.	NAME	MATERIAL
1	1	HANDLE	$\frac{3}{4}$ I.D. X 119" PIPE
2	2	HOSE HANGER	$\frac{1}{2}$ DIA. X $6\frac{1}{2}$ HR ROD
3	2	BACK SUPPORT	$\frac{3}{4}$ I.D. X $23\frac{1}{2}$" PIPE
4	2	SIDE BAR	$\frac{1}{2}$ I.D. X 42" PIPE
5	2	BRACE	$\frac{1}{4}$ X 1 X 18" FLAT
6	2	MOUNTING BRACKET	$\frac{1}{4}$ X 4 X 8" FLAT
7	1	AXLE	SEE # ⑦
8	1	TANK PLATE	$\frac{1}{4}$ X 12 X 24 HR PLATE

① $\frac{3}{4}$ I.D. X 119" BLACK PIPE HANDLE BENDING PROCEDURE: SEE SHOP DOLLY PROJECT.

② $\frac{1}{2}$ DIA. X $6\frac{1}{2}$ (2 REQ.)

③ $\frac{3}{4}$ I.D. X $23\frac{1}{2}$ BLACK PIPE (2 REQ.)

4" BACK BEND

$\frac{1}{4}$ DIA. EYE SCREW (3 REQ.) w/ SAFETY CHAIN & SNAP HOOKS TO SECURE TANKS.

$\phi \frac{1}{4}$ (3 P.)

④ $\frac{1}{2}$ I.D. X 42" BLACK PIPE (2 REQ.)

⑤ $\frac{1}{4}$ X 1 X 18" SCRIBE ENDS TO FIT ANGLE. (2 REQ.)

⑥ $\frac{1}{4}$ X 4 X 8" - 2" RADIUS AT END. (2 REQ.)

$\frac{5}{32}$ X $1\frac{1}{2}$ COTTER PIN (2 REQ.)

⑦ $\frac{3}{8}$ OR $\frac{3}{4}$ DIA. CRS AXLE. FIGURE LENGTH TO FIT FRAME & TWO WHEEL HUBS PLUS $\frac{1}{2}$" ON EACH END. APPROX. 31"

⑧ $\frac{1}{4}$ X 12 X 24" HR PLATE

AXLE ASSEMBLY PROCEDURE: SEE SHOP DOLLY PROJECT.

10" DIA. X 3" WHEEL w/ $\frac{5}{8}$ OR $\frac{3}{4}$ BEARING (2 REQ.)

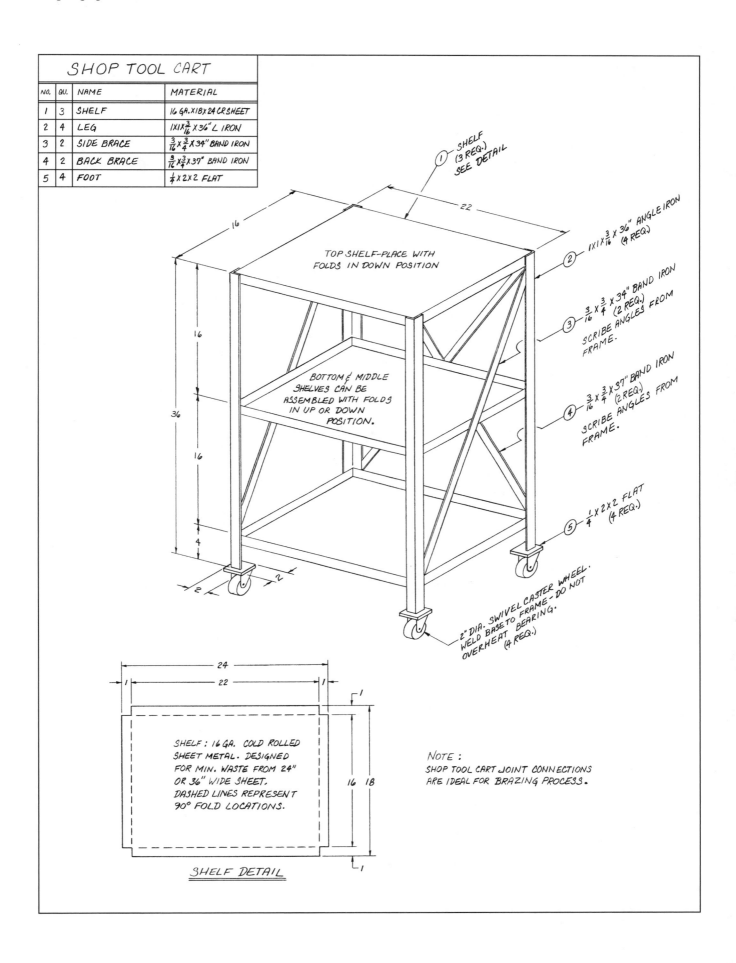

SHOP TOOL CART			
NO.	QU.	NAME	MATERIAL
1	3	SHELF	16 GA. X 18 X 24 CR SHEET
2	4	LEG	$1 \times 1 \times \frac{3}{16} \times 36"$ L IRON
3	2	SIDE BRACE	$\frac{3}{16} \times \frac{3}{4} \times 34"$ BAND IRON
4	2	BACK BRACE	$\frac{3}{16} \times \frac{3}{4} \times 37"$ BAND IRON
5	4	FOOT	$\frac{1}{4} \times 2 \times 2$ FLAT

① SHELF (3 REQ.) SEE DETAIL

② $1 \times 1 \times \frac{3}{16} \times 36"$ ANGLE IRON (4 REQ.)

③ $\frac{3}{16} \times \frac{3}{4} \times 34"$ BAND IRON (2 REQ.) SCRIBE ANGLES FROM FRAME.

④ $\frac{3}{16} \times \frac{3}{4} \times 37"$ BAND IRON (2 REQ.) SCRIBE ANGLES FROM FRAME.

⑤ $\frac{1}{4} \times 2 \times 2$ FLAT (4 REQ.)

TOP SHELF - PLACE WITH FOLDS IN DOWN POSITION

BOTTOM & MIDDLE SHELVES CAN BE ASSEMBLED WITH FOLDS IN UP OR DOWN POSITION.

2" DIA. SWIVEL CASTER WHEEL. WELD BASE TO FRAME - DO NOT OVERHEAT BEARING. (4 REQ.)

SHELF: 16 GA. COLD ROLLED SHEET METAL. DESIGNED FOR MIN. WASTE FROM 24" OR 36" WIDE SHEET. DASHED LINES REPRESENT 90° FOLD LOCATIONS.

SHELF DETAIL

NOTE:
SHOP TOOL CART JOINT CONNECTIONS ARE IDEAL FOR BRAZING PROCESS.

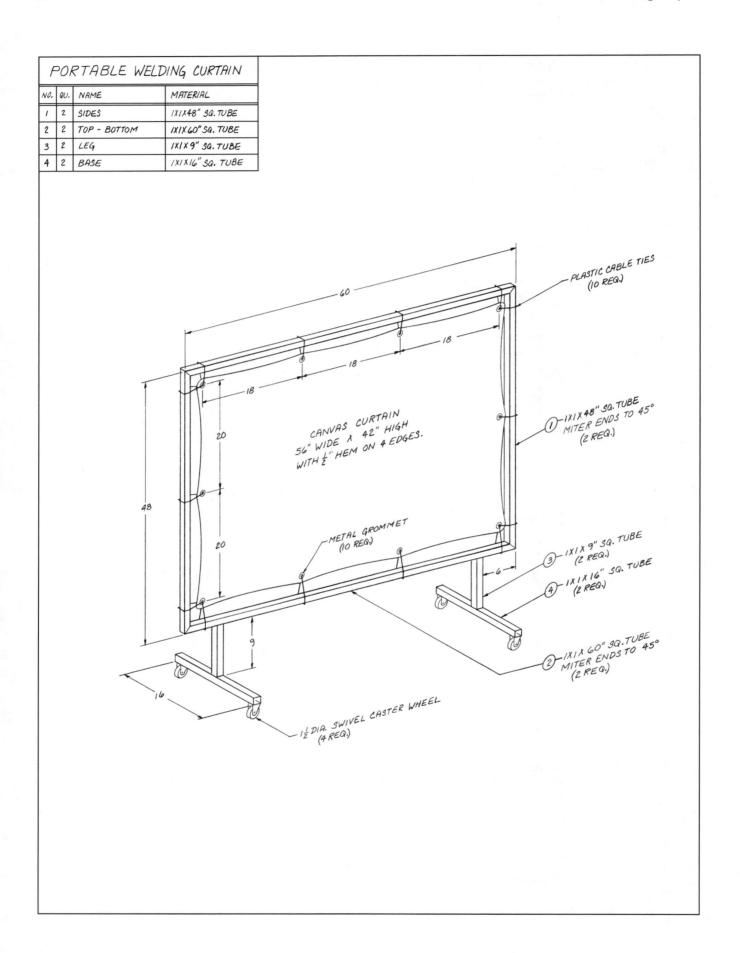

PORTABLE WELDING CURTAIN

NO.	QU.	NAME	MATERIAL
1	2	SIDES	1X1X48" SQ. TUBE
2	2	TOP - BOTTOM	1X1X60" SQ. TUBE
3	2	LEG	1X1X9" SQ. TUBE
4	2	BASE	1X1X16" SQ. TUBE

PLASTIC CABLE TIES (10 REQ.)

CANVAS CURTAIN 56" WIDE X 42" HIGH WITH ½" HEM ON 4 EDGES.

METAL GROMMET (10 REQ.)

① 1X1X48" SQ. TUBE MITER ENDS TO 45° (2 REQ.)

③ 1X1X9" SQ. TUBE (2 REQ.)

④ 1X1X16" SQ. TUBE (2 REQ.)

② 1X1X60" SQ. TUBE MITER ENDS TO 45° (2 REQ.)

1½ DIA. SWIVEL CASTER WHEEL (4 REQ.)

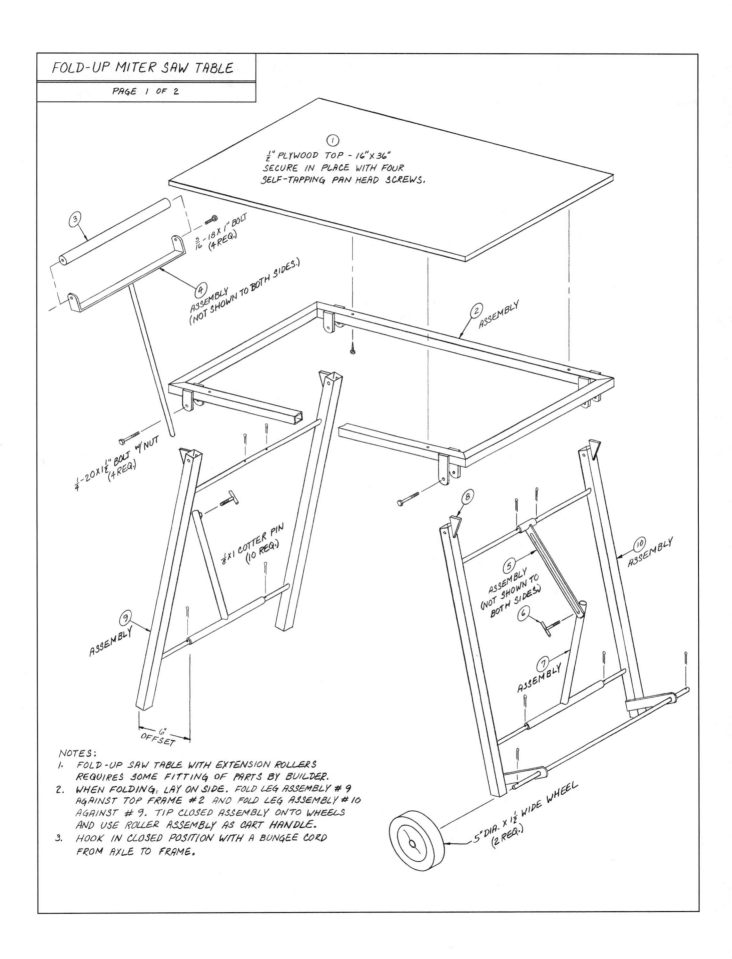

FOLD-UP MITER SAW TABLE

PAGE 1 OF 2

① ½" PLYWOOD TOP - 16" X 36"
SECURE IN PLACE WITH FOUR
SELF-TAPPING PAN HEAD SCREWS.

③

3/16 - 18 X 1" BOLT
(4 REQ.)

④ ASSEMBLY
(NOT SHOWN TO BOTH SIDES.)

② ASSEMBLY

¼ - 20 X 1¼" BOLT W/NUT
(4 REQ.)

⅛ X 1 COTTER PIN
(10 REQ.)

⑧

⑤ ASSEMBLY
(NOT SHOWN TO BOTH SIDES.)

⑥

⑩ ASSEMBLY

⑦ ASSEMBLY

⑨ ASSEMBLY

6"
OFFSET

5" DIA. X 1½ WIDE WHEEL
(2 REQ.)

NOTES:
1. FOLD-UP SAW TABLE WITH EXTENSION ROLLERS
   REQUIRES SOME FITTING OF PARTS BY BUILDER.
2. WHEN FOLDING, LAY ON SIDE. FOLD LEG ASSEMBLY # 9
   AGAINST TOP FRAME # 2 AND FOLD LEG ASSEMBLY # 10
   AGAINST # 9. TIP CLOSED ASSEMBLY ONTO WHEELS
   AND USE ROLLER ASSEMBLY AS CART HANDLE.
3. HOOK IN CLOSED POSITION WITH A BUNGEE CORD
   FROM AXLE TO FRAME.

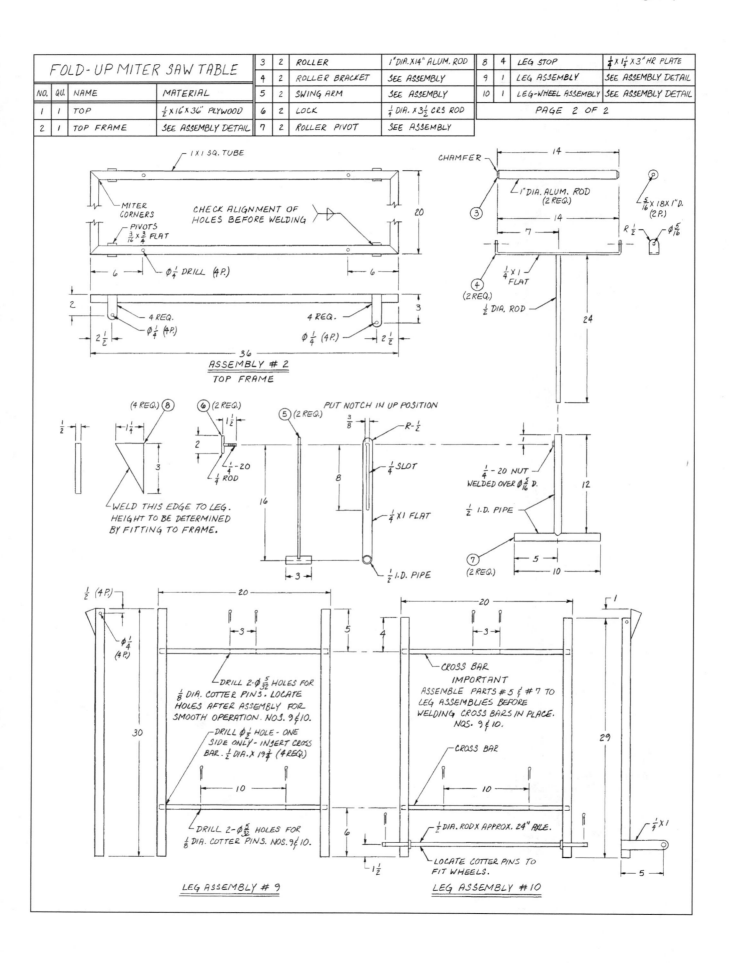

NO.	QU.	NAME	MATERIAL	3	2	ROLLER	1" DIA. X 14" ALUM. ROD	8	4	LEG STOP	$\frac{1}{4}$ X 1$\frac{1}{4}$ X 3" HR PLATE
				4	2	ROLLER BRACKET	SEE ASSEMBLY	9	1	LEG ASSEMBLY	SEE ASSEMBLY DETAIL
1	1	TOP	$\frac{1}{2}$ X 16 X 36" PLYWOOD	5	2	SWING ARM	SEE ASSEMBLY	10	1	LEG-WHEEL ASSEMBLY	SEE ASSEMBLY DETAIL
2	1	TOP FRAME	SEE ASSEMBLY DETAIL	6	2	LOCK	$\frac{1}{4}$ DIA. X 3$\frac{1}{2}$ CRS ROD				PAGE 2 OF 2
				7	2	ROLLER PIVOT	SEE ASSEMBLY				

FOLD-UP MITER SAW TABLE

ASSEMBLY # 2
TOP FRAME

LEG ASSEMBLY # 9

LEG ASSEMBLY # 10

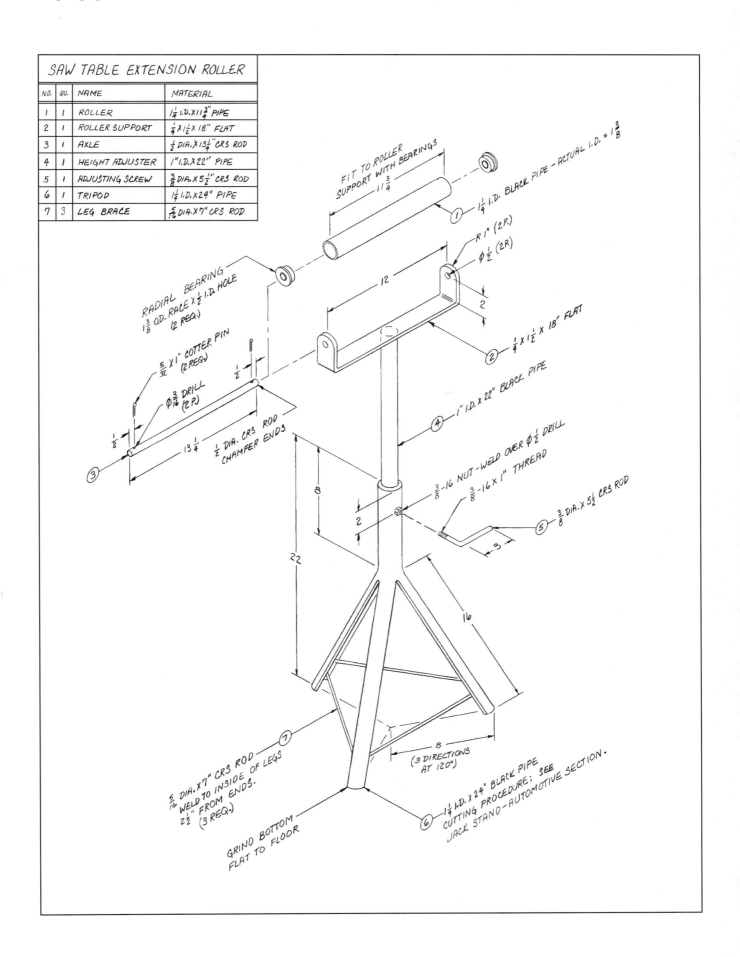

	SAW TABLE EXTENSION ROLLER		
NO.	QU.	NAME	MATERIAL
1	1	ROLLER	$1\frac{1}{4}$ I.D. X $11\frac{3}{4}$" PIPE
2	1	ROLLER SUPPORT	$\frac{1}{4}$ X $1\frac{1}{2}$ X 18" FLAT
3	1	AXLE	$\frac{1}{2}$ DIA. X $13\frac{1}{4}$" CRS ROD
4	1	HEIGHT ADJUSTER	1" I.D. X 22" PIPE
5	1	ADJUSTING SCREW	$\frac{3}{8}$ DIA. X $5\frac{1}{2}$" CRS ROD
6	1	TRIPOD	$1\frac{1}{4}$ I.D. X 24" PIPE
7	3	LEG BRACE	$\frac{5}{16}$ DIA. X 7" CRS ROD

FIT TO ROLLER SUPPORT WITH BEARINGS
$11\frac{3}{4}$

$1\frac{1}{4}$ I.D. BLACK PIPE - ACTUAL I.D. = $1\frac{3}{8}$

RADIAL BEARING
$1\frac{3}{8}$ O.D. RACE X $\frac{1}{2}$ I.D. HOLE
(2 REQ.)

$\frac{5}{32}$ X 1" COTTER PIN
(2 REQ.)

$\phi\frac{3}{16}$ DRILL
(2 P.)

R 1" (2P.)
$\phi\frac{1}{2}$ (2P.)

12

2

$\frac{1}{4}$ X $1\frac{1}{2}$ X 18" FLAT

$\frac{1}{2}$

$\frac{1}{2}$

$13\frac{1}{4}$

$\frac{1}{2}$ DIA. CRS ROD
CHAMFER ENDS

1" I.D. X 22" BLACK PIPE

$\frac{3}{8}$-16 NUT - WELD OVER $\phi\frac{1}{2}$ DRILL

$\frac{3}{8}$-16 X 1" THREAD

$\frac{3}{8}$ DIA. X $5\frac{1}{2}$" CRS ROD

3

8

2

22

16

$\frac{5}{16}$ DIA. X 7" CRS ROD
WELD TO INSIDE OF LEGS
$2\frac{1}{2}$" FROM ENDS.
(3 REQ.)

GRIND BOTTOM
FLAT TO FLOOR

8
(3 DIRECTIONS
AT 120°)

$1\frac{1}{4}$ I.D. X 24" BLACK PIPE
CUTTING PROCEDURE; SEE
JACK STAND - AUTOMOTIVE SECTION.

NO.	QU.	NAME	MATERIAL								
		DRYWALL STILTS		3	2	FOOT – BASE	7×10×16 GA. SHEET	8	2	FOOT PADS	¼×3×3½ RUBBER PAD
				4	1	HEEL BRACKET	4½×6×16 GA. SHEET			PAGE 1 OF 2	
1	1	LEG SUPPORT	3×10×16 GA. SHEET	5	1	TOE BRACKET	2×4×16 GA. SHEET			MATERIAL X 2 FOR SET	
2	1	SIDE SUPPORT	¾ I.D.×37" THIN WALL	6	2	LEGS	SEE ASSEMBLY				
				7	1	STABILIZER	SEE ASSEMBLY				

2" X 30" DOG COLLAR

10-24 ROUND HEAD SCREW WITH NUT. (2 REQ.)

½ X 8 PAN HEAD SCREW (2 REQ.)

5/16 X 1½ HEX BOLT

1" X 20" DOG COLLAR

1" X 24" DOG COLLAR

5/16 X ¾ HEX BOLT (5 REQ.)

5/16 X 2" HEX BOLT WITH NUT

③ (2 REQ.)

⑥ (2 REQ.)

⑧ (2 REQ.)

5/16 X ¾ HEX BOLT (4 REQ.)

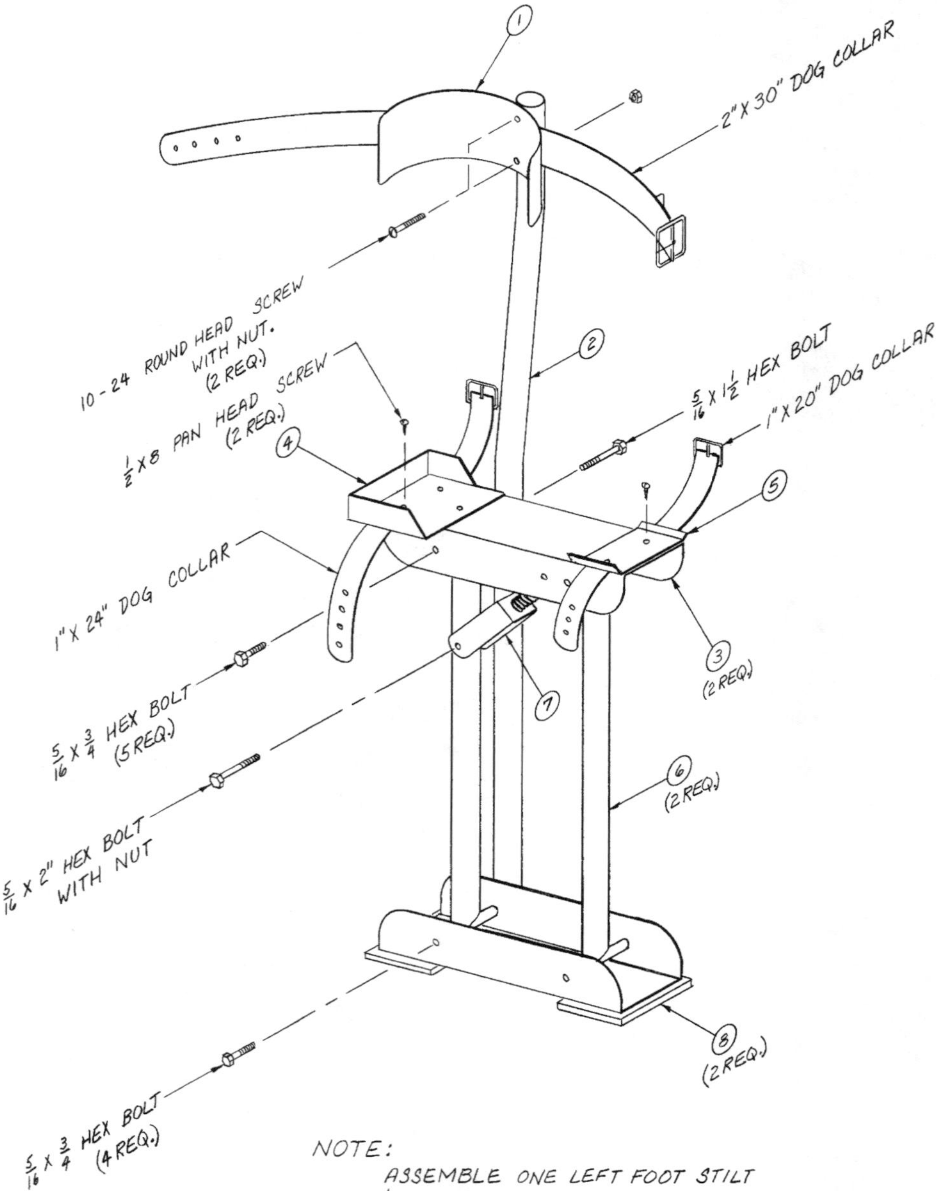

NOTE:
   ASSEMBLE ONE LEFT FOOT STILT
   & ONE RIGHT FOOT STILT.

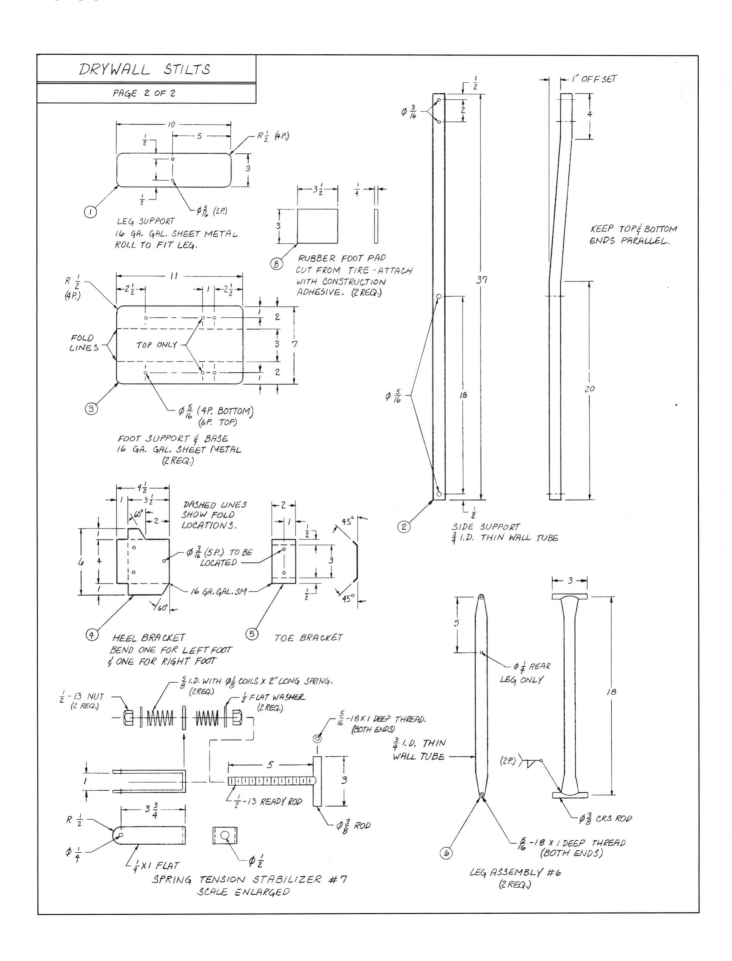

DRYWALL STILTS

PAGE 2 OF 2

① LEG SUPPORT
16 GA. GAL. SHEET METAL
ROLL TO FIT LEG.

R½ (4P.)
½
5
10
3
½
Ø 3/16 (2P.)

⑧ RUBBER FOOT PAD
CUT FROM TIRE - ATTACH
WITH CONSTRUCTION
ADHESIVE. (2 REQ.)
3½   ¼   3

③ FOOT SUPPORT & BASE
16 GA. GAL. SHEET METAL
(2 REQ.)
R½ (4P.)
FOLD LINES
TOP ONLY
11   2½   1   2½   1
2   3   2   7
Ø 5/16 (4P. BOTTOM) (6P. TOP)

④ HEEL BRACKET
BEND ONE FOR LEFT FOOT
& ONE FOR RIGHT FOOT
DASHED LINES SHOW FOLD LOCATIONS.
4½   1   3½   60°   2
6   4
Ø 3/16 (5P.) TO BE LOCATED
16 GA. GAL. SM
60°

⑤ TOE BRACKET
2   1   ½   45°   3   ½   45°

SPRING TENSION STABILIZER #7
SCALE ENLARGED
½ -13 NUT (2 REQ.)
5/8 I.D. WITH Ø 1/8 COILS X 2" LONG SPRING. (2REQ.)
½ FLAT WASHER (2 REQ.)
5/16 -18 X 1 DEEP THREAD. (BOTH ENDS)
5
½ -13 READY ROD
Ø 3/8 ROD
1
R ½
3 3/4
Ø ¼
¼ X 1 FLAT
Ø ½

② SIDE SUPPORT
¾ I.D. THIN WALL TUBE
½
2
Ø 3/16
37
Ø 5/16
18
½
1" OFFSET
4
KEEP TOP & BOTTOM ENDS PARALLEL.
20

⑥ LEG ASSEMBLY #6
(2 REQ.)
3
5
18
Ø ¼ REAR LEG ONLY
¾ I.D. THIN WALL TUBE
(2P.)
Ø 3/8 CRS ROD
5/16 -18 X 1 DEEP THREAD (BOTH ENDS)

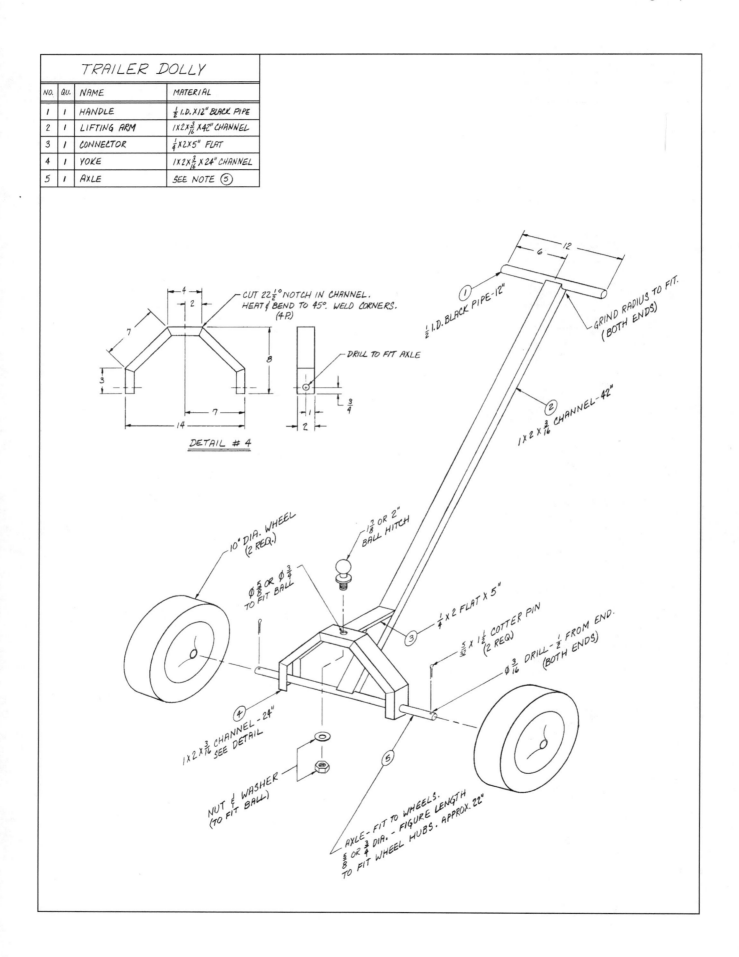

TRAILER DOLLY			
NO.	QU.	NAME	MATERIAL
1	1	HANDLE	$\frac{1}{2}$ I.D. X12" BLACK PIPE
2	1	LIFTING ARM	1X2X$\frac{3}{16}$ X42" CHANNEL
3	1	CONNECTOR	$\frac{1}{4}$X2X5" FLAT
4	1	YOKE	1X2X$\frac{3}{16}$ X 24" CHANNEL
5	1	AXLE	SEE NOTE ⑤

CUT 22$\frac{1}{2}$° NOTCH IN CHANNEL.
HEAT & BEND TO 45°. WELD CORNERS.
(4 P.)

DRILL TO FIT AXLE

DETAIL # 4

$\frac{1}{2}$ I.D. BLACK PIPE-12"

GRIND RADIUS TO FIT.
(BOTH ENDS)

1 X 2 X $\frac{3}{16}$ CHANNEL-42"

10" DIA. WHEEL
(2 REQ.)

$\emptyset \frac{5}{8}$ OR $\emptyset \frac{3}{4}$
TO FIT BALL

1$\frac{7}{8}$ OR 2"
BALL HITCH

$\frac{1}{4}$ X 2 FLAT X 5"

$\frac{5}{32}$ X 1$\frac{1}{2}$ COTTER PIN
(2 REQ)

$\emptyset \frac{3}{16}$ DRILL - $\frac{1}{2}$ FROM END.
(BOTH ENDS)

1 X 2 X $\frac{3}{16}$ CHANNEL - 24"
SEE DETAIL

NUT & WASHER
(TO FIT BALL)

AXLE - FIT TO WHEELS.
$\frac{5}{8}$ OR $\frac{3}{4}$ DIA. - FIGURE LENGTH
TO FIT WHEEL HUBS. APPROX. 22"

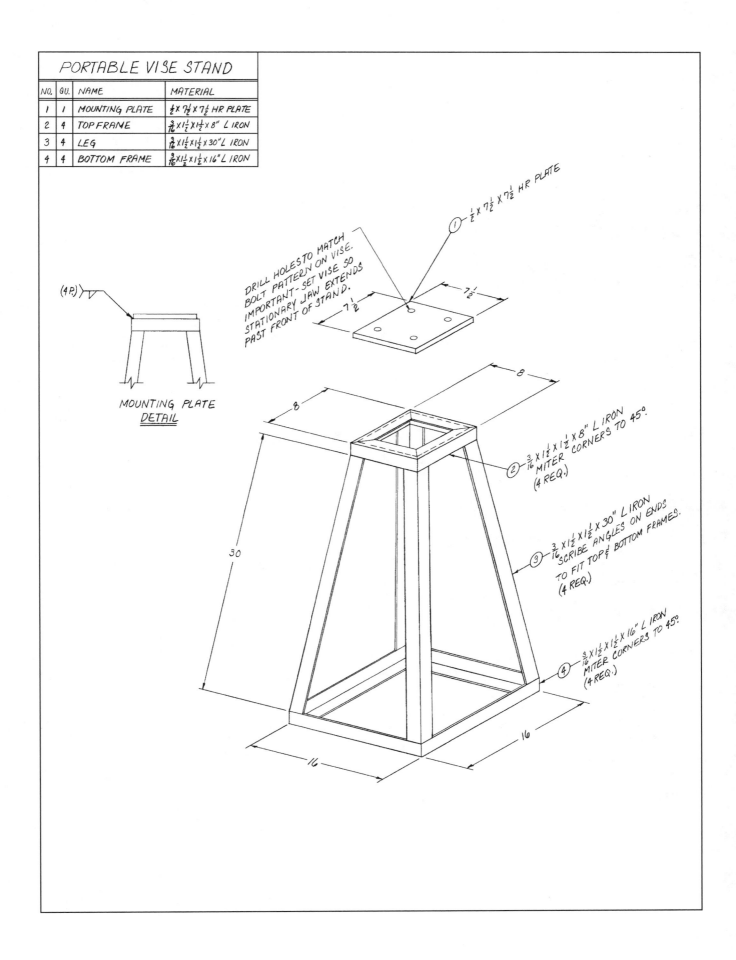

PORTABLE VISE STAND			
NO.	QU.	NAME	MATERIAL
1	1	MOUNTING PLATE	$\frac{1}{2}$ X $7\frac{1}{2}$ X $7\frac{1}{2}$ HR PLATE
2	4	TOP FRAME	$\frac{3}{16}$ X $1\frac{1}{2}$ X $1\frac{1}{2}$ X 8" L IRON
3	4	LEG	$\frac{3}{16}$ X $1\frac{1}{2}$ X $1\frac{1}{2}$ X 30" L IRON
4	4	BOTTOM FRAME	$\frac{3}{16}$ X $1\frac{1}{2}$ X $1\frac{1}{2}$ X 16" L IRON

(4 P.)

MOUNTING PLATE
DETAIL

① $\frac{1}{2}$ X $7\frac{1}{2}$ X $7\frac{1}{2}$ HR PLATE

DRILL HOLES TO MATCH BOLT PATTERN ON VISE. IMPORTANT- SET VISE SO STATIONARY JAW EXTENDS PAST FRONT OF STAND.

$7\frac{1}{2}$

$7\frac{1}{2}$

8

8

② $\frac{3}{16}$ X $1\frac{1}{2}$ X $1\frac{1}{2}$ X 8" L IRON MITER CORNERS TO 45°. (4 REQ.)

30

③ $\frac{3}{16}$ X $1\frac{1}{2}$ X $1\frac{1}{2}$ X 30" L IRON SCRIBE ANGLES ON ENDS TO FIT TOP & BOTTOM FRAMES. (4 REQ.)

④ $\frac{3}{16}$ X $1\frac{1}{2}$ X $1\frac{1}{2}$ X 16" L IRON MITER CORNERS TO 45°. (4 REQ.)

16

16

Auto Equipment

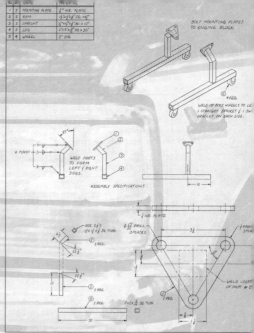

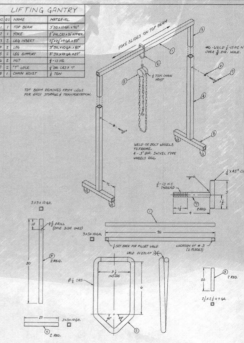

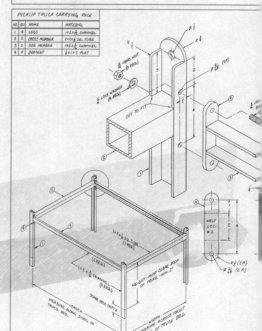

ENGINE STAND				6	2	PIVOT BRACE	$\frac{1}{4}$ PLATE	14	1	MOUNTING PLATE	$\frac{1}{2}$" THICK STEEL PLATE
				7	1	COVER PLATE	$\frac{1}{4}$ PLATE	15	4	HEX. NUT	$\frac{1}{2}$-13 NC
NO.	QU.	NAME	MATERIAL	8	1	PIVOT BEARING	2" I.D. PIPE x 9"	16	4	FLAT WASHER	$\frac{1}{2}$ DIA.
1	1	UPRIGHT	3"SQ.x 10 GA. x 30"	9	1	LOCK NUT	$\frac{5}{8}$-18-NF NUT	17	4	HEX. BOLT	$\frac{1}{2}$-13NC x 3"
2	1	REAR SUPPORT	3" SQ.x 10 GA. x 30"	10	1	PIVOT LOCK	$\frac{5}{8}$ D. CRS x 9"	18A	8	ARM EXTENDERS	$\frac{3}{8}$ x 1$\frac{1}{2}$ x 7 CRS
3	1	CENTER SUPPORT	3" SQ. x 10 GA. x 36"	11	1	PIVOT AXLE	2" DIA. CRS x 12$\frac{1}{4}$"	18B	4	SLOT SPACER	$\frac{1}{2}$ x $\frac{1}{2}$ x 1$\frac{1}{2}$ STEEL
4	1	FRONT SUPPORT	3"SQ. x 10 GA. x 24"	12	1	PIVOT HANDLE	$\frac{3}{4}$ DIA. CRS x 24"	18C	4	ENGINE MOUNT	1"DIA. x 3" CRS
5	1	BRACE	2x1x$\frac{3}{16}$x17" CHANNEL	13	2	END CAP	1$\frac{1}{2}$ DIA. CRS x 2"	19	4	WHEELS	3" DIA.

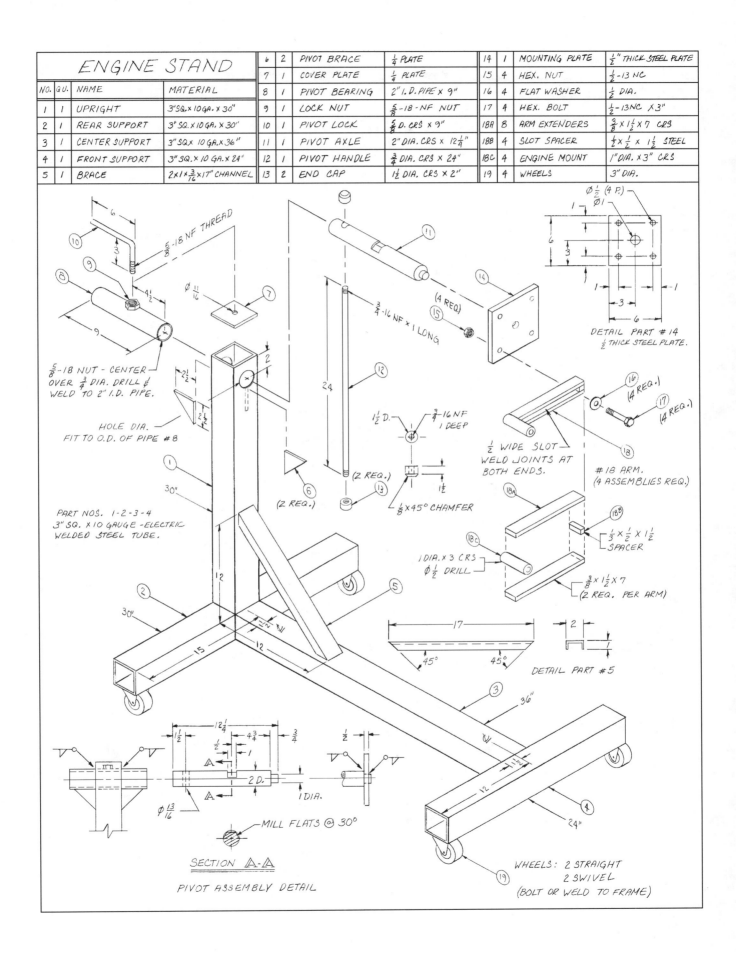

$\frac{5}{8}$-18 NF THREAD

$\emptyset$ $\frac{11}{16}$

$\frac{5}{8}$-18 NUT - CENTER OVER $\frac{3}{4}$ DIA. DRILL & WELD TO 2" I.D. PIPE.

HOLE DIA. FIT TO O.D. OF PIPE #8

PART NOS. 1-2-3-4 3" SQ. x 10 GAUGE -ELECTRIC WELDED STEEL TUBE.

$\frac{3}{4}$-16 NF x 1 LONG

(4 REQ.)

DETAIL PART #14 $\frac{1}{2}$ THICK STEEL PLATE.

1$\frac{1}{2}$ D. $\frac{3}{4}$-16 NF 1 DEEP

$\frac{1}{8}$ x 45° CHAMFER

(2 REQ.)

(2 REQ.)

$\frac{1}{2}$ WIDE SLOT WELD JOINTS AT BOTH ENDS.

#18 ARM. (4 ASSEMBLIES REQ.)

$\frac{1}{2}$ x $\frac{1}{2}$ x 1$\frac{1}{2}$ SPACER

1 DIA. x 3 CRS $\emptyset$ $\frac{1}{2}$ DRILL

$\frac{3}{8}$ x 1$\frac{1}{2}$ x 7 (2 REQ. PER ARM)

DETAIL PART #5

PART NOS. 1-2-3-4 (see diagram)

$\emptyset$ $\frac{13}{16}$

MILL FLATS @ 30°

SECTION A-A

PIVOT ASSEMBLY DETAIL

WHEELS: 2 STRAIGHT 2 SWIVEL (BOLT OR WELD TO FRAME)

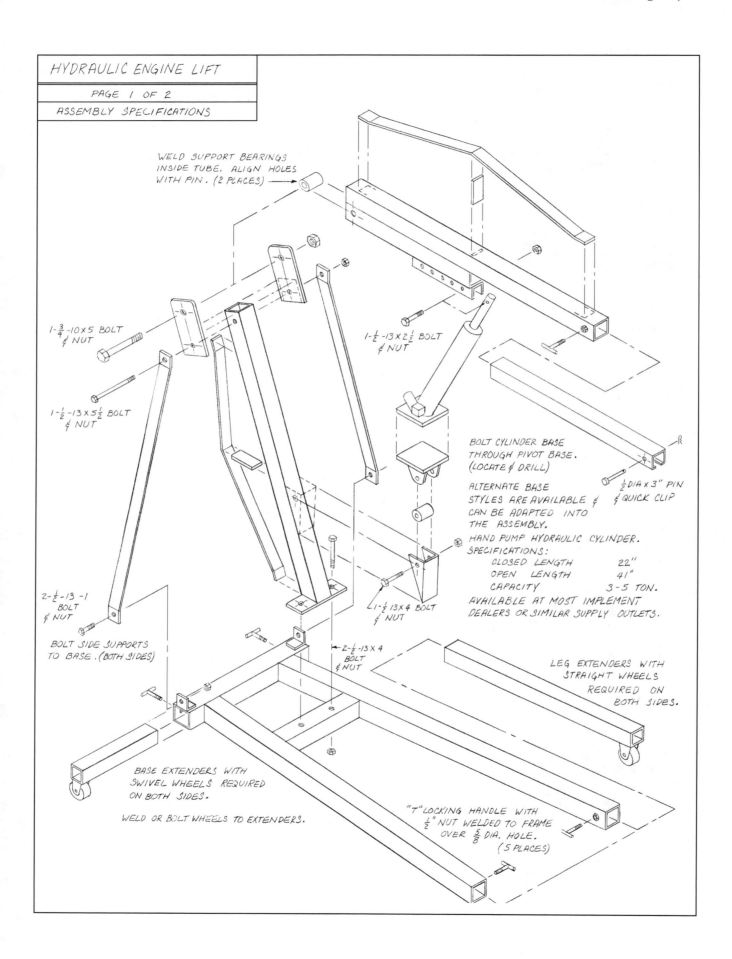

HYDRAULIC ENGINE LIFT

PAGE 1 OF 2

ASSEMBLY SPECIFICATIONS

WELD SUPPORT BEARINGS INSIDE TUBE. ALIGN HOLES WITH PIN. (2 PLACES)

$1 - \frac{3}{4} - 10 \times 5$ BOLT & NUT

$1 - \frac{1}{2} - 13 \times 5\frac{1}{2}$ BOLT & NUT

$1 - \frac{1}{2} - 13 \times 2\frac{1}{2}$ BOLT & NUT

$2 - \frac{1}{2} - 13 - 1$ BOLT & NUT

BOLT SIDE SUPPORTS TO BASE. (BOTH SIDES)

$1 - \frac{1}{2} - 13 \times 4$ BOLT & NUT

$2 - \frac{1}{2} - 13 \times 4$ BOLT & NUT

BOLT CYLINDER BASE THROUGH PIVOT BASE. (LOCATE & DRILL)

ALTERNATE BASE STYLES ARE AVAILABLE & CAN BE ADAPTED INTO THE ASSEMBLY.

$\frac{1}{2}$ DIA × 3" PIN & QUICK CLIP

HAND PUMP HYDRAULIC CYLINDER. SPECIFICATIONS:
CLOSED LENGTH   22"
OPEN   LENGTH   41"
CAPACITY   3 - 5 TON.
AVAILABLE AT MOST IMPLEMENT DEALERS OR SIMILAR SUPPLY OUTLETS.

LEG EXTENDERS WITH STRAIGHT WHEELS REQUIRED ON BOTH SIDES.

BASE EXTENDERS WITH SWIVEL WHEELS REQUIRED ON BOTH SIDES.

WELD OR BOLT WHEELS TO EXTENDERS.

"T" LOCKING HANDLE WITH $\frac{1}{2}$" NUT WELDED TO FRAME OVER $\frac{5}{8}$ DIA. HOLE. (5 PLACES)

\multicolumn{2}{l}{HYDRAULIC ENGINE LIFT}			

HYDRAULIC ENGINE LIFT

BASE

NO.	QU.	NAME	MATERIAL
1	2	LEG	3" SQ.X 10 GA. X 60"
2	2	LEG EXTENSION	2½" SQ. X 7 GA. X 40"
3	1	UPRIGHT SUPPORT	3" SQ.X 10 GA. X 14½"
4	1	BACK SUPPORT	3" SQ.X 10 GA. X 24"
5	1	BACK EXTENSION	2½" SQ.X 7 GA. X 15"
6	2	SIDE BRACKET	2X2X¼X2 L IRON

UPRIGHT

1	1	SUPPORT BOW	¼ X 2 X 48"
2	1	SPACER	¼ X 2 X 4½"
3	2	PIVOT PLATE	½ X 4 X 10"
4	1	UPRIGHT	3" SQ.X 10 GA.X 48"
5	1	CYLINDER SUPPORT	3" SQ.X 10 GA. X 9"
6	1	PIVOT BEARING	1½ DIA. X 2¾"
7	1	CYLINDER BRACKET	¼ H.R. PLATE
8	1	BASE PLATE	½ X 3 X 9"
9	2	SIDE BRACES	¼ X 2 X 48"

BOOM

1	1	SUPPORT BOW	¼ X 2 X 48"
2	1	SPACER	¼ X 2 X 4½"
3	1	BOOM	3" SQ.X 10 GA. X 50"
4	1	BOOM EXTENSION	2½" SQ.X 7 GA. X 40"
5	1	BOOM SUPPORT	3" SQ.X 10 GA. X 25"
6	1	PIVOT BEARING	1½ DIA. X 2¾"
7	1	RAM BRACKET	2 X 2" SQ. X 12"

PAGE 2 OF 2

PART SPECIFICATIONS

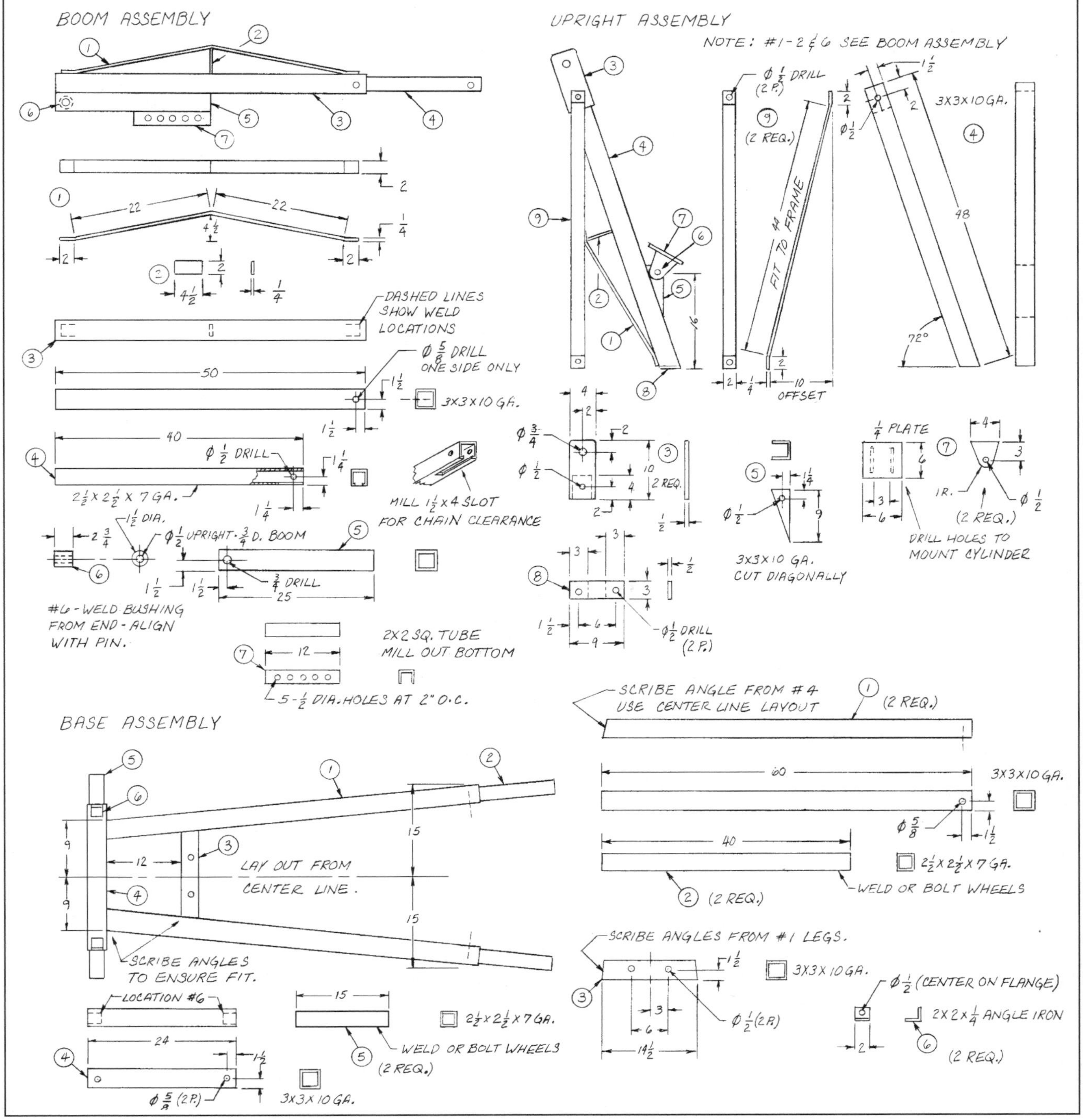

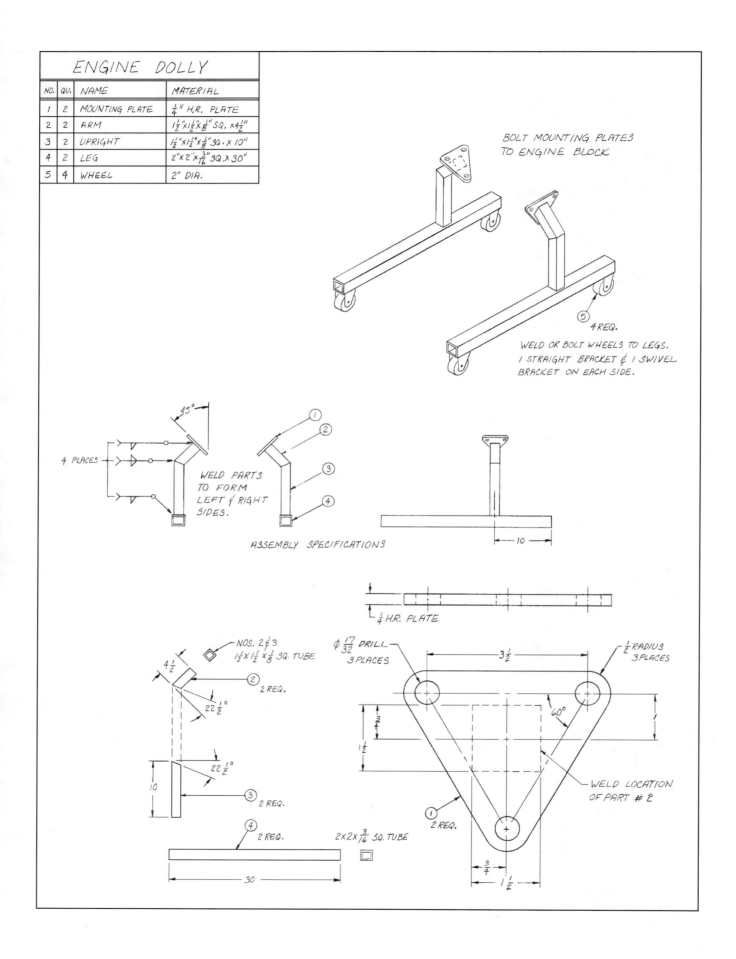

ENGINE DOLLY

NO.	QU.	NAME	MATERIAL
1	2	MOUNTING PLATE	$\frac{1}{4}$" H.R. PLATE
2	2	ARM	$1\frac{1}{2}$"×$1\frac{1}{2}$"×$\frac{1}{8}$" SQ. ×$4\frac{1}{2}$"
3	2	UPRIGHT	$1\frac{1}{2}$"×$1\frac{1}{2}$"×$\frac{1}{8}$" SQ. × 10"
4	2	LEG	2"×2"×$\frac{3}{16}$" SQ. × 30"
5	4	WHEEL	2" DIA.

BOLT MOUNTING PLATES
TO ENGINE BLOCK

⑤ 4 REQ.

WELD OR BOLT WHEELS TO LEGS.
1 STRAIGHT BRACKET & 1 SWIVEL
BRACKET ON EACH SIDE.

45°

4 PLACES

WELD PARTS
TO FORM
LEFT & RIGHT
SIDES.

ASSEMBLY SPECIFICATIONS

10

$\frac{1}{4}$ H.R. PLATE

NOS. 2 & 3
$1\frac{1}{2}$×$1\frac{1}{2}$×$\frac{1}{8}$ SQ. TUBE

$4\frac{1}{2}$

② 2 REQ.

$22\frac{1}{2}$°

$22\frac{1}{2}$°

10

③ 2 REQ.

④ 2 REQ.

2×2×$\frac{3}{16}$ SQ. TUBE

$\phi\frac{17}{32}$ DRILL
3 PLACES

$3\frac{1}{2}$

$\frac{1}{2}$ RADIUS
3 PLACES

60°

$\frac{3}{4}$

$1\frac{1}{2}$

WELD LOCATION
OF PART # 2

① 2 REQ.

$\frac{3}{4}$

$1\frac{1}{2}$

30

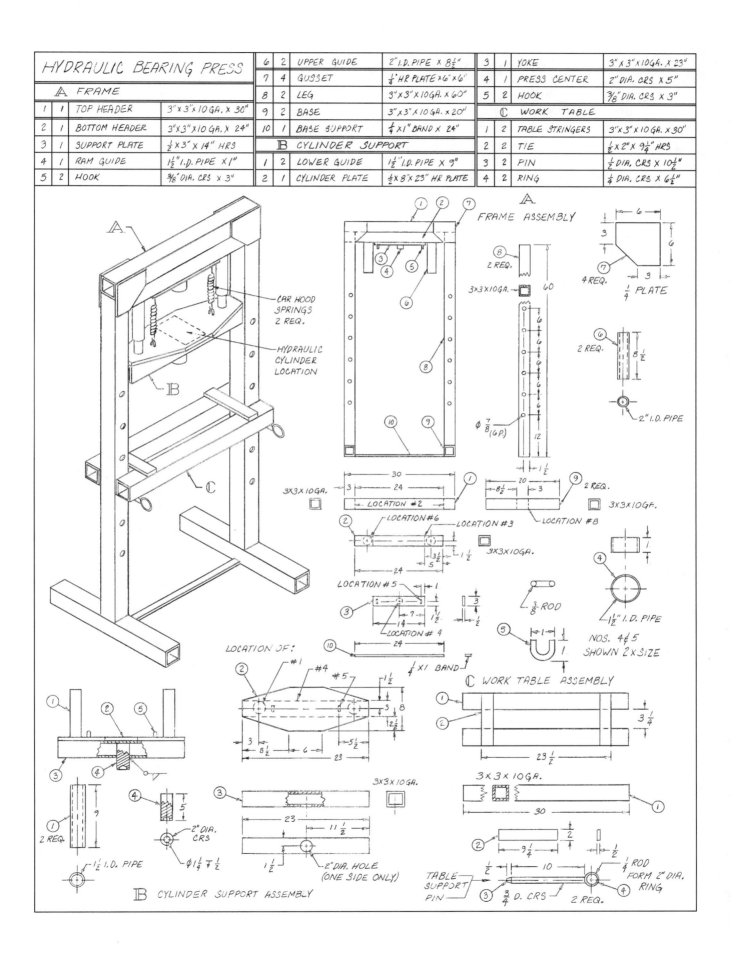

HYDRAULIC BEARING PRESS

		A FRAME	
1	1	TOP HEADER	3"x 3"x 10 GA. x 30"
2	1	BOTTOM HEADER	3"x 3"x 10 GA. x 24"
3	1	SUPPORT PLATE	½ x 3" x 14" HRS
4	1	RAM GUIDE	1½" I.D. PIPE x 1"
5	2	HOOK	⅜" DIA. CRS x 3"
6	2	UPPER GUIDE	2" I.D. PIPE x 8½"
7	4	GUSSET	¼" HR PLATE x 6" x 6"
8	2	LEG	3"x 3"x 10 GA. x 60"
9	2	BASE	3"x 3"x 10 GA. x 20"
10	1	BASE SUPPORT	¼ x 1" BAND x 24"

		B CYLINDER SUPPORT	
1	2	LOWER GUIDE	1½" I.D. PIPE x 9"
2	1	CYLINDER PLATE	½ x 8" x 23" HR PLATE

3	1	YOKE	3"x 3"x 10 GA. x 23"
4	1	PRESS CENTER	2" DIA. CRS x 5"
5	2	HOOK	⅜" DIA. CRS x 3"

		C WORK TABLE	
1	2	TABLE STRINGERS	3"x 3"x 10 GA. x 30"
2	2	TIE	½ x 2" x 9¼" HRS
3	2	PIN	½ DIA. CRS x 10½"
4	2	RING	¼ DIA. CRS x 6½"

A FRAME ASSEMBLY

CAR HOOD SPRINGS 2 REQ.

HYDRAULIC CYLINDER LOCATION

¼ PLATE

2 REQ. 8 ½

2" I.D. PIPE

3x3x10GA. 60

φ ⅞ (6P.) 12

LOCATION #2

LOCATION #6

LOCATION #3

LOCATION #8

LOCATION #5

LOCATION #4

⅜ ROD

1½" I.D. PIPE

NOS. 4 & 5 SHOWN 2 x SIZE

LOCATION OF:
#1 #4 #5

¼ X 1 BAND

C WORK TABLE ASSEMBLY

B CYLINDER SUPPORT ASSEMBLY

1½" I.D. PIPE

2" DIA. CRS

φ 1¼ ⊤ ½

2" DIA. HOLE (ONE SIDE ONLY)

3x3x10GA.

TABLE SUPPORT PIN

¼ ROD FORM 2" DIA. RING

¾ D. CRS

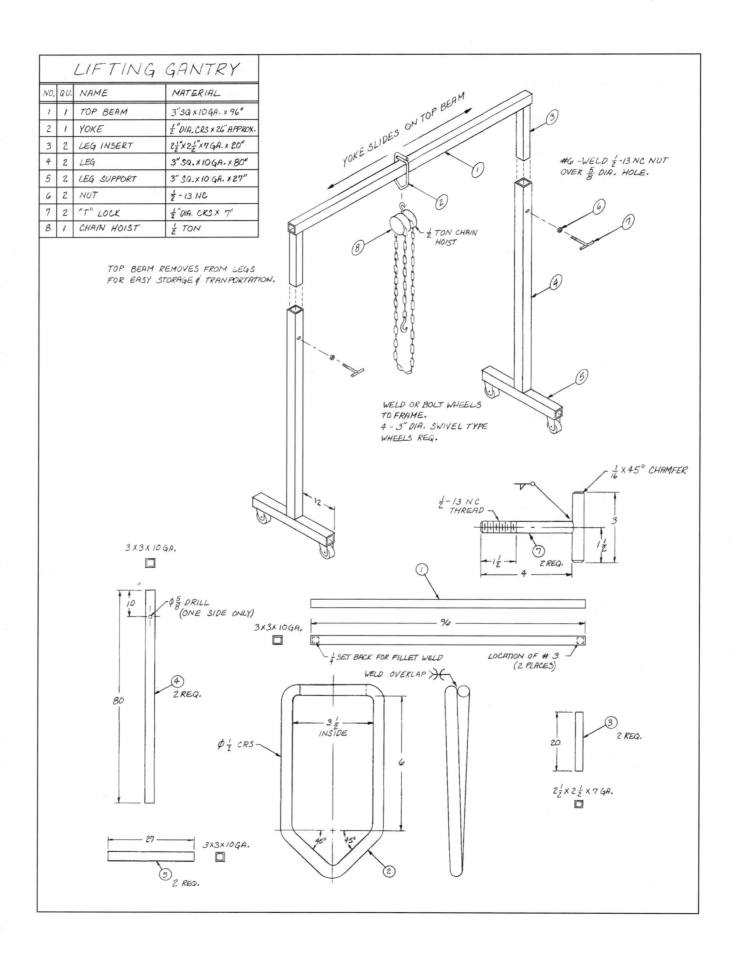

LIFTING GANTRY

NO.	QU.	NAME	MATERIAL
1	1	TOP BEAM	3" SQ x 10 GA. x 96"
2	1	YOKE	$\frac{1}{2}$" DIA. CRS x 26" APPROX.
3	2	LEG INSERT	$2\frac{1}{2}$" x $2\frac{1}{2}$" x 7 GA. x 20"
4	2	LEG	3" SQ. x 10 GA. x 80"
5	2	LEG SUPPORT	3" SQ. x 10 GA. x 27"
6	2	NUT	$\frac{1}{2}$ - 13 NC
7	2	"T" LOCK	$\frac{1}{2}$" DIA. CRS x 7"
8	1	CHAIN HOIST	$\frac{1}{2}$ TON

YOKE SLIDES ON TOP BEAM

#6 -WELD $\frac{1}{2}$-13 NC NUT OVER $\frac{5}{8}$ DIA. HOLE.

$\frac{1}{2}$ TON CHAIN HOIST

TOP BEAM REMOVES FROM LEGS FOR EASY STORAGE & TRANSPORTATION.

WELD OR BOLT WHEELS TO FRAME.
4 - 3" DIA. SWIVEL TYPE WHEELS REQ.

$\frac{1}{16}$ X 45° CHAMFER

$\frac{1}{2}$ - 13 N C THREAD

3
$1\frac{1}{2}$

$1\frac{1}{2}$
4
2 REQ.

12

3 X 3 X 10 GA.

10

$\phi \frac{5}{8}$ DRILL (ONE SIDE ONLY)

3 X 3 X 10 GA.

96

$\frac{1}{4}$ SET BACK FOR FILLET WELD

LOCATION OF # 3 (2 PLACES)

WELD OVERLAP

4
2 REQ.

80

$3\frac{1}{2}$ INSIDE

$\phi \frac{1}{2}$ CRS

6

45°   45°

3
2 REQ.

20

$2\frac{1}{2}$ x $2\frac{1}{2}$ x 7 GA.

27

3 X 3 X 10 GA.

5
2 REQ.

2

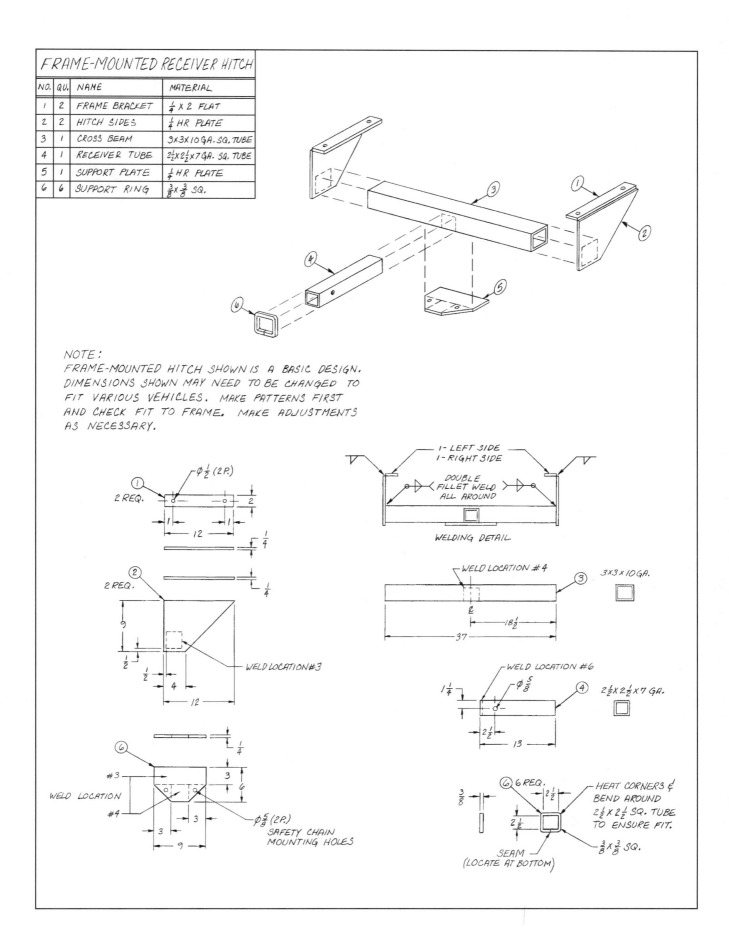

FRAME-MOUNTED RECEIVER HITCH

NO.	QU.	NAME	MATERIAL
1	2	FRAME BRACKET	$\frac{1}{4}$ X 2 FLAT
2	2	HITCH SIDES	$\frac{1}{4}$ HR PLATE
3	1	CROSS BEAM	3X3X10 GA. SQ. TUBE
4	1	RECEIVER TUBE	$2\frac{1}{2}$ X $2\frac{1}{2}$ X7 GA. SQ. TUBE
5	1	SUPPORT PLATE	$\frac{1}{4}$ HR PLATE
6	6	SUPPORT RING	$\frac{3}{8}$ X $\frac{3}{8}$ SQ.

NOTE:
FRAME-MOUNTED HITCH SHOWN IS A BASIC DESIGN.
DIMENSIONS SHOWN MAY NEED TO BE CHANGED TO
FIT VARIOUS VEHICLES. MAKE PATTERNS FIRST
AND CHECK FIT TO FRAME. MAKE ADJUSTMENTS
AS NECESSARY.

$\phi \frac{1}{2}$ (2 P.)

1 2 REQ.

1   12   1

2

$\frac{1}{4}$

1 - LEFT SIDE
1 - RIGHT SIDE
DOUBLE
FILLET WELD
ALL AROUND

WELDING DETAIL

2 2 REQ.

$\frac{1}{4}$

9

$\frac{1}{2}$

$\frac{1}{2}$

4

12

WELD LOCATION #3

WELD LOCATION #4

3   3X3X10 GA.

$\frac{1}{2}$

$18\frac{1}{2}$

37

WELD LOCATION #6

$1\frac{1}{4}$

$\phi \frac{5}{8}$

4   $2\frac{1}{2}$ X $2\frac{1}{2}$ X 7 GA.

$2\frac{1}{2}$

13

6

$\frac{1}{4}$

#3

3

6

WELD LOCATION

#4

3

3

9

$\phi \frac{5}{8}$ (2 P.)
SAFETY CHAIN
MOUNTING HOLES

6 6 REQ.

$2\frac{1}{2}$

$\frac{3}{8}$

$2\frac{1}{2}$

HEAT CORNERS &
BEND AROUND
$2\frac{1}{2}$ X $2\frac{1}{2}$ SQ. TUBE
TO ENSURE FIT.

$\frac{3}{8}$ X $\frac{3}{8}$ SQ.

SEAM
(LOCATE AT BOTTOM)

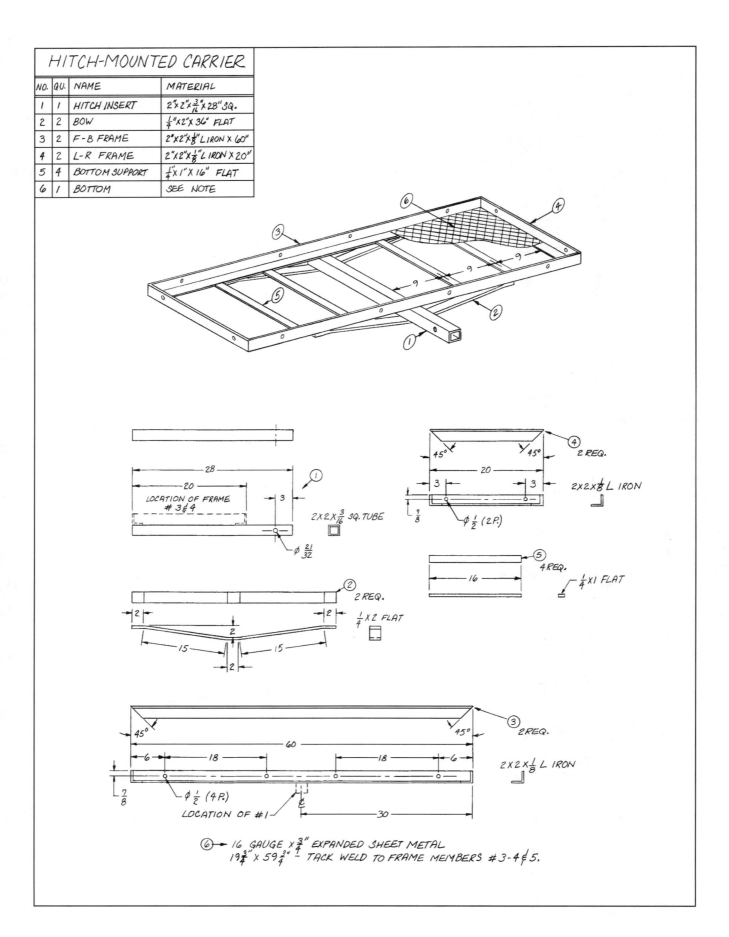

HITCH-MOUNTED CARRIER

NO.	QU.	NAME	MATERIAL
1	1	HITCH INSERT	$2''x2''x\frac{3}{16}''x28''$ SQ.
2	2	BOW	$\frac{1}{4}''x2''x36''$ FLAT
3	2	F-B FRAME	$2''x2''x\frac{1}{8}''$ L IRON X 60''
4	2	L-R FRAME	$2''x2''x\frac{1}{8}''$ L IRON X 20''
5	4	BOTTOM SUPPORT	$\frac{1}{4}''x1''x16''$ FLAT
6	1	BOTTOM	SEE NOTE

28

20

LOCATION OF FRAME #3 & 4

3

$2x2x\frac{3}{16}$ SQ. TUBE

$\phi \frac{21}{32}$

45°   45°   ④ 2 REQ.

20

3   3

$\frac{7}{8}$

$\phi \frac{1}{2}$ (2 P.)

$2x2x\frac{1}{8}$ L IRON

⑤ 4 REQ.

16

$\frac{1}{4} x1$ FLAT

② 2 REQ.

2   2

2

2

15   15

2

$\frac{1}{4} x2$ FLAT

45°   45°   ③ 2 REQ.

60

6   18   18   6

$\frac{7}{8}$

$\phi \frac{1}{2}$ (4 P.)

LOCATION OF #1

30

$2x2x\frac{1}{8}$ L IRON

⑥→ 16 GAUGE $x\frac{3}{4}''$ EXPANDED SHEET METAL
$19\frac{3}{4}'' \times 59\frac{3}{4}''$ - TACK WELD TO FRAME MEMBERS #3-4 & 5.

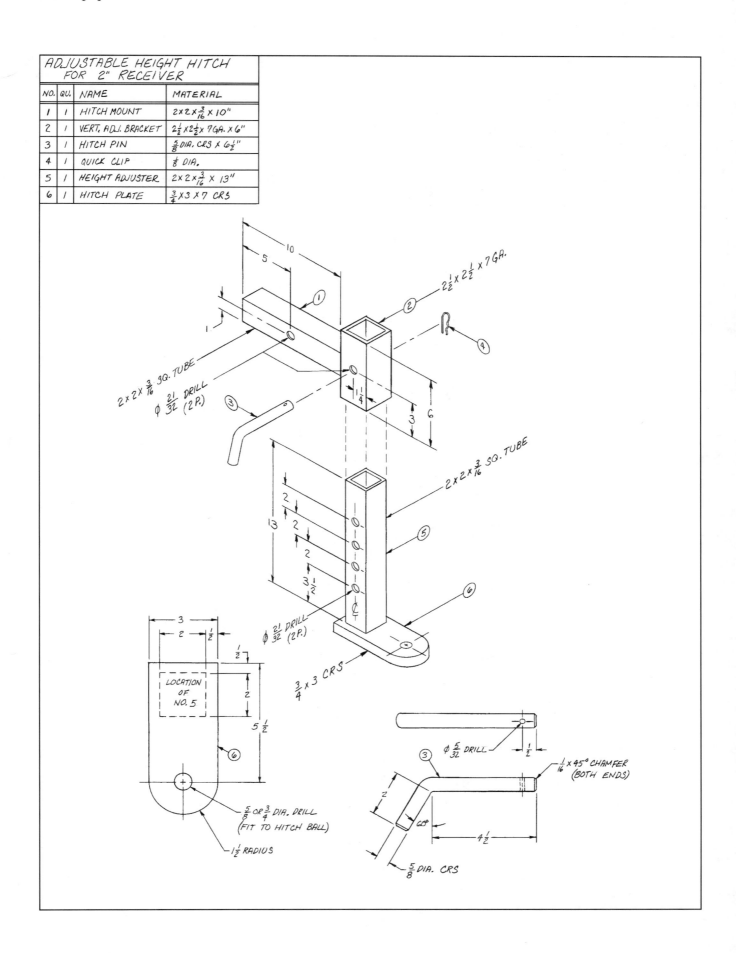

ADJUSTABLE HEIGHT HITCH FOR 2" RECEIVER

NO.	QU.	NAME	MATERIAL
1	1	HITCH MOUNT	$2 \times 2 \times \frac{3}{16} \times 10"$
2	1	VERT. ADJ. BRACKET	$2\frac{1}{2} \times 2\frac{1}{2} \times 7 GA. \times 6"$
3	1	HITCH PIN	$\frac{5}{8}$ DIA. CRS $\times 6\frac{1}{2}"$
4	1	QUICK CLIP	$\frac{1}{8}$ DIA.
5	1	HEIGHT ADJUSTER	$2 \times 2 \times \frac{3}{16} \times 13"$
6	1	HITCH PLATE	$\frac{3}{4} \times 3 \times 7$ CRS

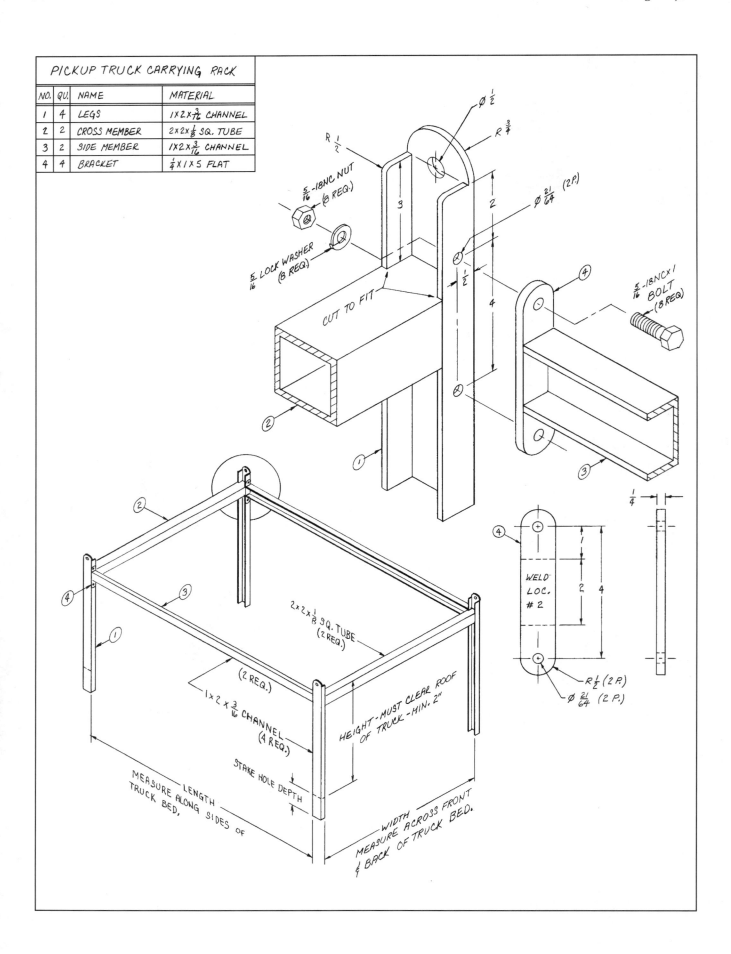

PICKUP TRUCK CARRYING RACK

NO.	QU.	NAME	MATERIAL
1	4	LEGS	1X2X$\frac{3}{16}$ CHANNEL
2	2	CROSS MEMBER	2X2X$\frac{1}{8}$ SQ. TUBE
3	2	SIDE MEMBER	1X2X$\frac{3}{16}$ CHANNEL
4	4	BRACKET	$\frac{1}{4}$X1X5 FLAT

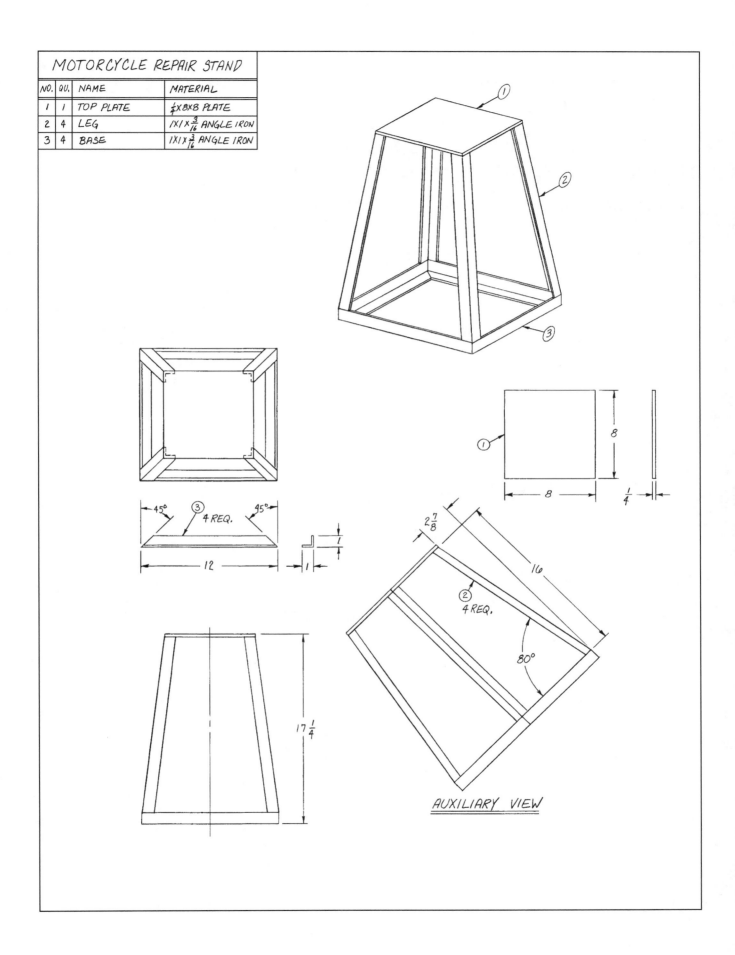

MOTORCYCLE REPAIR STAND

NO.	QU.	NAME	MATERIAL
1	1	TOP PLATE	$\frac{1}{4}$ X 8 X 8 PLATE
2	4	LEG	1X1X$\frac{3}{16}$ ANGLE IRON
3	4	BASE	1X1X$\frac{3}{16}$ ANGLE IRON

AUXILIARY VIEW

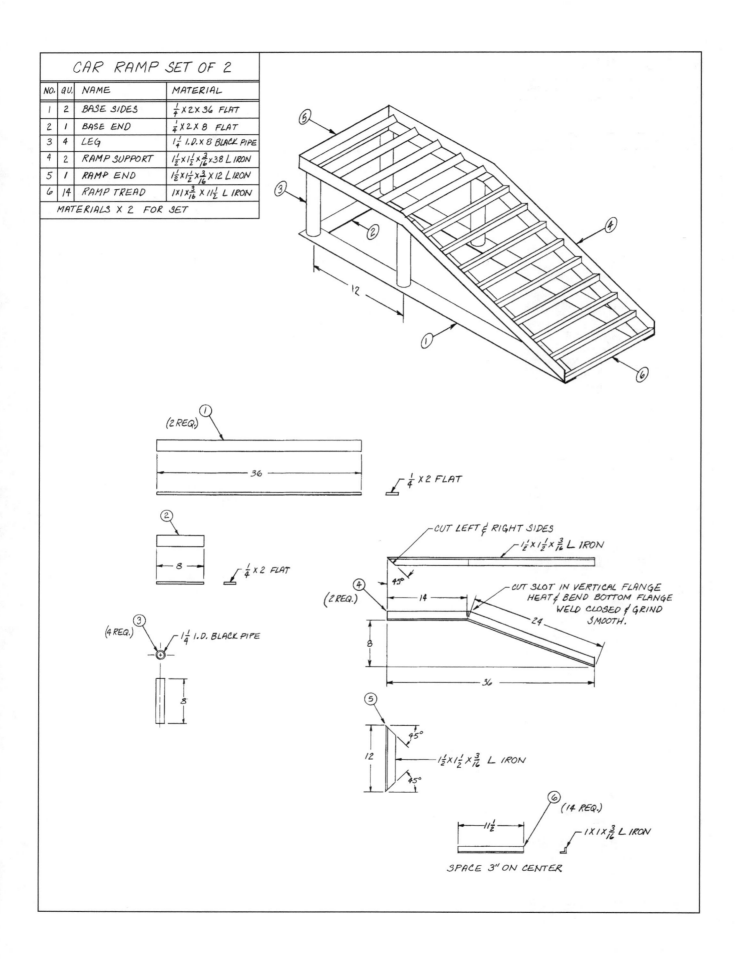

CAR RAMP SET OF 2			
NO.	QU.	NAME	MATERIAL
1	2	BASE SIDES	$\frac{1}{4}$ X 2 X 36 FLAT
2	1	BASE END	$\frac{1}{4}$ X 2 X 8 FLAT
3	4	LEG	$1\frac{1}{4}$ I.D. X 8 BLACK PIPE
4	2	RAMP SUPPORT	$1\frac{1}{2}$ X $1\frac{1}{2}$ X $\frac{3}{16}$ X 38 L IRON
5	1	RAMP END	$1\frac{1}{2}$ X $1\frac{1}{2}$ X $\frac{3}{16}$ X 12 L IRON
6	14	RAMP TREAD	1 X 1 X $\frac{3}{16}$ X $11\frac{1}{2}$ L IRON
MATERIALS X 2 FOR SET			

(2 REQ.)

36

$\frac{1}{4}$ X 2 FLAT

8

$\frac{1}{4}$ X 2 FLAT

(4 REQ.) $1\frac{1}{4}$ I.D. BLACK PIPE

8

CUT LEFT & RIGHT SIDES

$1\frac{1}{2}$ X $1\frac{1}{2}$ X $\frac{3}{16}$ L IRON

45°

(2 REQ.)   14

CUT SLOT IN VERTICAL FLANGE
HEAT & BEND BOTTOM FLANGE
WELD CLOSED & GRIND
SMOOTH.

24

8

36

45°

12

$1\frac{1}{2}$ X $1\frac{1}{2}$ X $\frac{3}{16}$ L IRON

45°

(14 REQ.)

$11\frac{1}{2}$

1 X 1 X $\frac{3}{16}$ L IRON

SPACE 3" ON CENTER

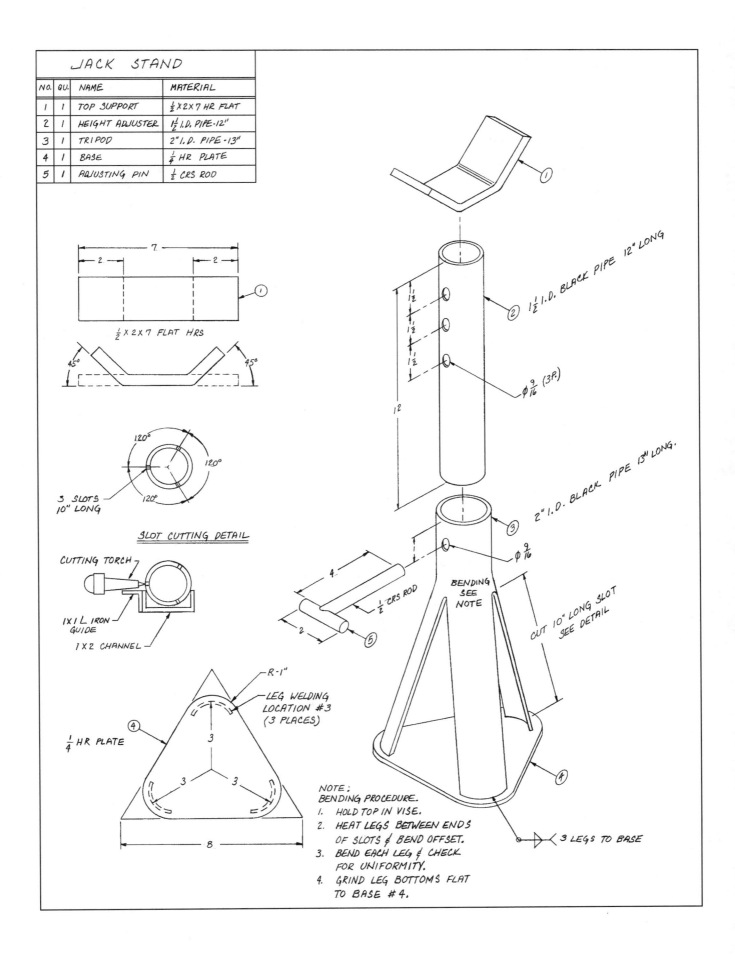

JACK STAND			
NO.	QU.	NAME	MATERIAL
1	1	TOP SUPPORT	½ X 2 X 7 HR FLAT
2	1	HEIGHT ADJUSTER	1½ I.D. PIPE - 12"
3	1	TRIPOD	2" I.D. PIPE - 13"
4	1	BASE	¼ HR PLATE
5	1	ADJUSTING PIN	½ CRS ROD

½ X 2 X 7 FLAT HRS

45°   45°

3 SLOTS 10" LONG

120°   120°   120°

SLOT CUTTING DETAIL

CUTTING TORCH

1 X 1 L IRON GUIDE

1 X 2 CHANNEL

R - 1"

LEG WELDING LOCATION #3 (3 PLACES)

¼ HR PLATE

1½ I.D. BLACK PIPE 12" LONG

φ 9/16 (3 P.)

2" I.D. BLACK PIPE 13" LONG.

φ 9/16

½ CRS ROD

BENDING SEE NOTE

CUT 10" LONG SLOT SEE DETAIL

NOTE;
BENDING PROCEDURE.
1. HOLD TOP IN VISE.
2. HEAT LEGS BETWEEN ENDS OF SLOTS & BEND OFFSET.
3. BEND EACH LEG & CHECK FOR UNIFORMITY.
4. GRIND LEG BOTTOMS FLAT TO BASE #4.

3 LEGS TO BASE

NO.	QU.	NAME	MATERIAL
1	2	MOUNTING BRKT.	$\frac{1}{2}$ X 2 X 9" HR FLAT
2	2	EXTENDER	2 X 3 X 8" TUBE
3	1	STEP SUPPORT	2 X 3 X 56" TUBE
4	1	STEP	2" I.D. X 75" PIPE

PICKUP TRUCK DOOR STEP

MATERIALS X 2 FOR SET

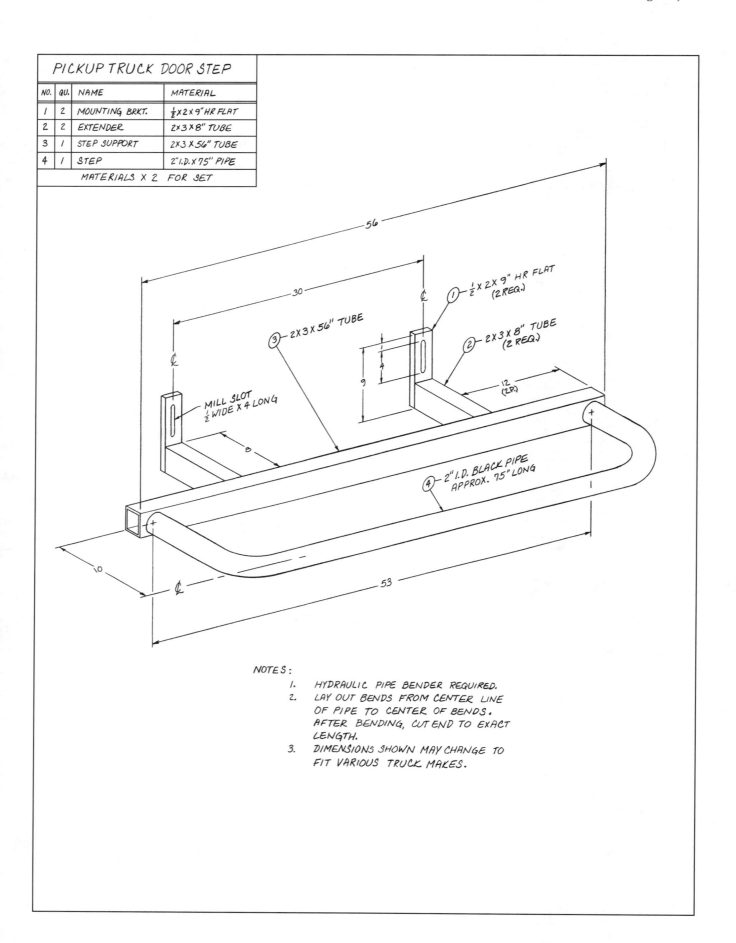

56

30

③ 2 X 3 X 56" TUBE

① $\frac{1}{2}$ X 2 X 9" HR FLAT (2 REQ.)

② 2 X 3 X 8" TUBE (2 REQ.)

9

4

MILL SLOT $\frac{1}{2}$ WIDE X 4 LONG

12 (2 P.)

8

④ 2" I.D. BLACK PIPE APPROX. 75" LONG

10

53

NOTES:
1. HYDRAULIC PIPE BENDER REQUIRED.
2. LAY OUT BENDS FROM CENTER LINE OF PIPE TO CENTER OF BENDS. AFTER BENDING, CUT END TO EXACT LENGTH.
3. DIMENSIONS SHOWN MAY CHANGE TO FIT VARIOUS TRUCK MAKES.

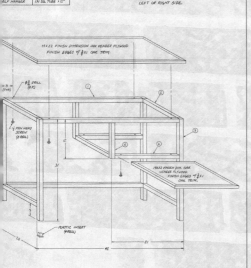

Home Equipment

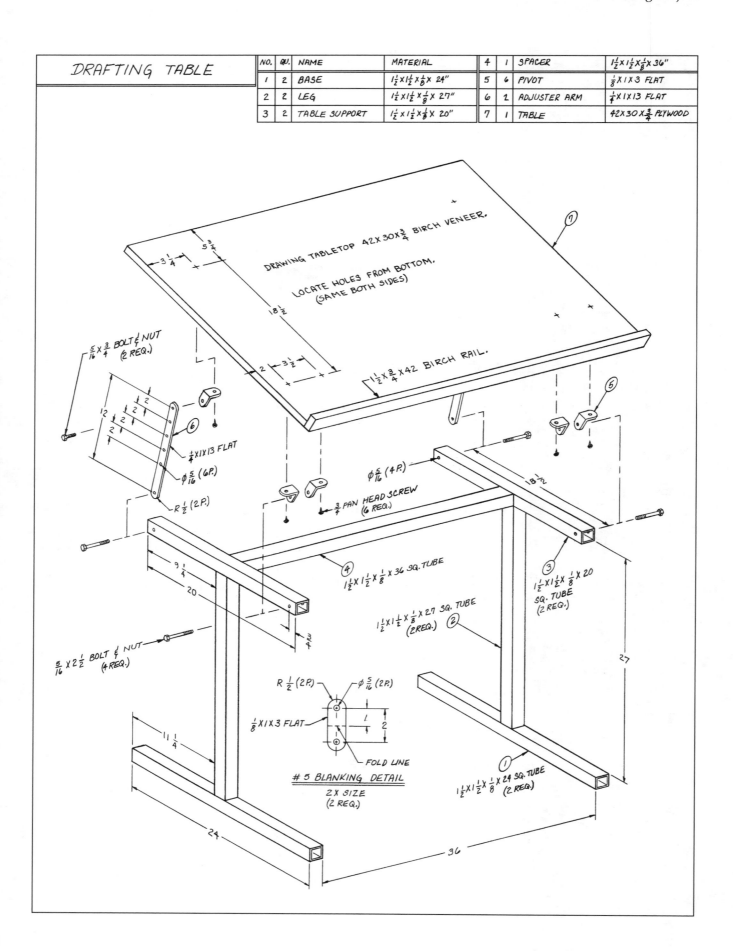

DRAFTING TABLE

NO.	QU.	NAME	MATERIAL				
				4	1	SPACER	$1\frac{1}{2} \times 1\frac{1}{2} \times \frac{1}{8} \times 36''$
1	2	BASE	$1\frac{1}{2} \times 1\frac{1}{2} \times \frac{1}{8} \times 24''$	5	6	PIVOT	$\frac{1}{8} \times 1 \times 3$ FLAT
2	2	LEG	$1\frac{1}{2} \times 1\frac{1}{2} \times \frac{1}{8} \times 27''$	6	1	ADJUSTER ARM	$\frac{1}{4} \times 1 \times 13$ FLAT
3	2	TABLE SUPPORT	$1\frac{1}{2} \times 1\frac{1}{2} \times \frac{1}{8} \times 20''$	7	1	TABLE	$42 \times 30 \times \frac{3}{4}$ PLYWOOD

DRAWING TABLETOP $42 \times 30 \times \frac{3}{4}$ BIRCH VENEER.

LOCATE HOLES FROM BOTTOM.
(SAME BOTH SIDES)

$\frac{5}{16} \times \frac{3}{4}$ BOLT & NUT
(2 REQ.)

$1\frac{1}{2} \times \frac{3}{4} \times 42$ BIRCH RAIL.

$\frac{1}{4} \times 1 \times 13$ FLAT

$\phi \frac{5}{16}$ (6 P.)

$R \frac{1}{2}$ (2 P.)

$\phi \frac{5}{16}$ (4 P.)

$\frac{3}{4}$ PAN HEAD SCREW
(6 REQ.)

$\frac{5}{16} \times 2\frac{1}{2}$ BOLT & NUT
(4 REQ.)

$1\frac{1}{2} \times 1\frac{1}{2} \times \frac{1}{8} \times 36$ SQ. TUBE

$1\frac{1}{2} \times 1\frac{1}{2} \times \frac{1}{8} \times 27$ SQ. TUBE
(2 REQ.)

$1\frac{1}{2} \times 1\frac{1}{2} \times \frac{1}{8} \times 20$ SQ. TUBE
(2 REQ.)

$R \frac{1}{2}$ (2 P.) $\phi \frac{5}{16}$ (2 P.)

$\frac{1}{8} \times 1 \times 3$ FLAT

FOLD LINE

#5 BLANKING DETAIL
2X SIZE
(2 REQ.)

$1\frac{1}{2} \times 1\frac{1}{2} \times \frac{1}{8} \times 24$ SQ. TUBE
(2 REQ.)

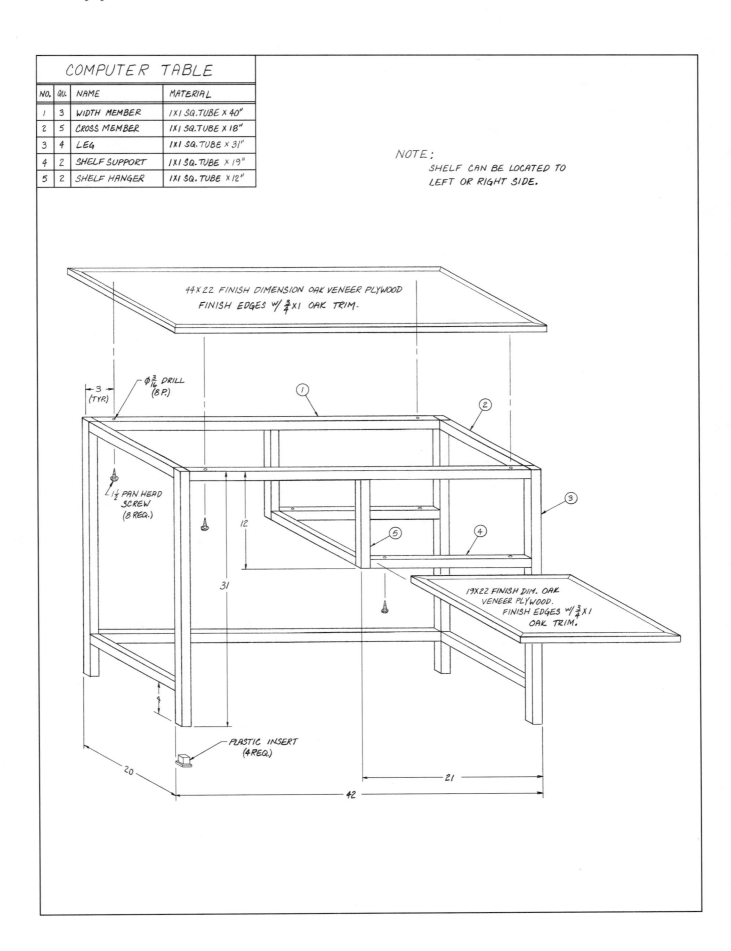

COMPUTER TABLE

NO.	QU.	NAME	MATERIAL
1	3	WIDTH MEMBER	1X1 SQ.TUBE X 40"
2	5	CROSS MEMBER	1X1 SQ.TUBE X 18"
3	4	LEG	1X1 SQ.TUBE X 31"
4	2	SHELF SUPPORT	1X1 SQ.TUBE X 19"
5	2	SHELF HANGER	1X1 SQ. TUBE X 12"

NOTE:
SHELF CAN BE LOCATED TO
LEFT OR RIGHT SIDE.

44X22 FINISH DIMENSION OAK VENEER PLYWOOD
FINISH EDGES W/ $\frac{3}{4}$ X1 OAK TRIM.

3 (TYP.)

$\phi \frac{3}{16}$ DRILL (8 P.)

$1\frac{1}{2}$ PAN HEAD SCREW (8 REQ.)

12

31

19X22 FINISH DIM. OAK VENEER PLYWOOD. FINISH EDGES W/ $\frac{3}{4}$ X1 OAK TRIM.

PLASTIC INSERT (4 REQ.)

20

21

42

NO.	QU.	NAME	MATERIAL
		GUITAR STAND	
1	1	NECK REST	$\frac{1}{4}$ DIA. x 10" HRS
2	2	NECK GUARD	$\frac{3}{8}$ I.D. x 4" FUEL HOSE
3	1	NECK SUPPORT	$\frac{1}{2}$ DIA. x 24" HRS
4	1	UPRIGHT	$\frac{1}{2}$ I.D. x 13" PIPE
5	1	BODY REST	$\frac{1}{4}$ DIA. x 21" HRS
6	2	BODY GUARD	$\frac{3}{8}$ I.D. x 10" FUEL HOSE
7	2	REAR LEG	$\frac{1}{2}$ I.D. x 12" PIPE
8	1	FRONT LEG	$\frac{1}{2}$ I.D. x 8" PIPE

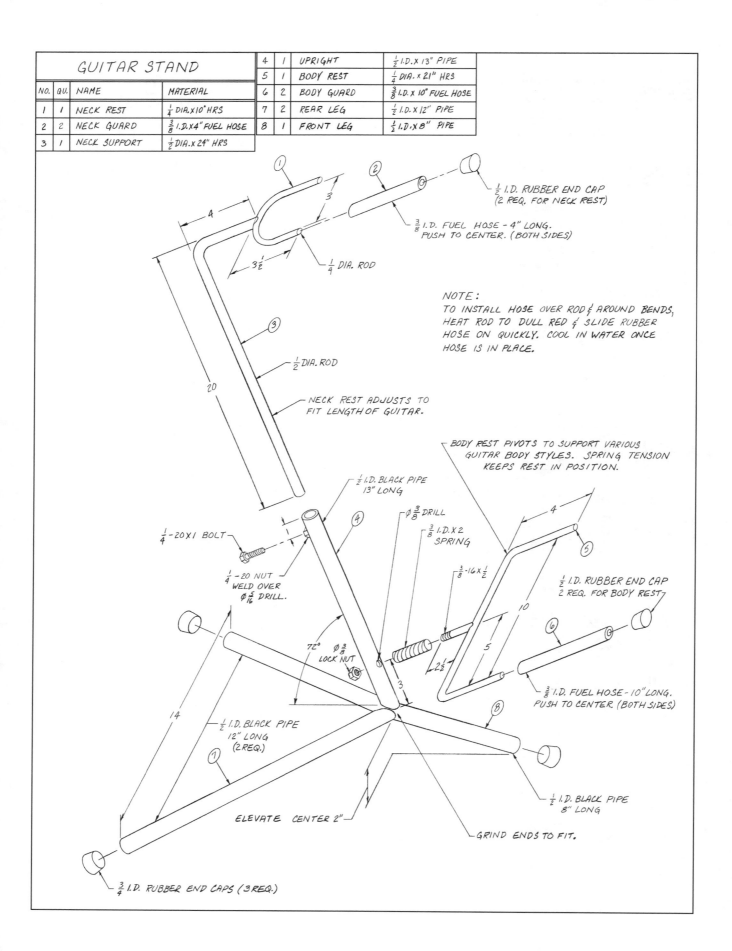

$\frac{1}{2}$ I.D. RUBBER END CAP (2 REQ. FOR NECK REST)

$\frac{3}{8}$ I.D. FUEL HOSE – 4" LONG. PUSH TO CENTER. (BOTH SIDES)

$\frac{1}{4}$ DIA. ROD

NOTE:
TO INSTALL HOSE OVER ROD & AROUND BENDS, HEAT ROD TO DULL RED & SLIDE RUBBER HOSE ON QUICKLY. COOL IN WATER ONCE HOSE IS IN PLACE.

$\frac{1}{2}$ DIA. ROD

NECK REST ADJUSTS TO FIT LENGTH OF GUITAR.

BODY REST PIVOTS TO SUPPORT VARIOUS GUITAR BODY STYLES. SPRING TENSION KEEPS REST IN POSITION.

$\frac{1}{2}$ I.D. BLACK PIPE 13" LONG

$\varnothing \frac{3}{8}$ DRILL

$\frac{3}{8}$ I.D. x 2 SPRING

$\frac{1}{4}$-20 x 1 BOLT

$\frac{1}{4}$-20 NUT WELD OVER $\varnothing \frac{5}{16}$ DRILL.

$\frac{3}{8}$-16 x $\frac{1}{2}$

$\frac{1}{2}$ I.D. RUBBER END CAP 2 REQ. FOR BODY REST

72° $\varnothing \frac{3}{8}$ LOCK NUT

$2\frac{1}{2}$

$\frac{3}{8}$ I.D. FUEL HOSE – 10" LONG. PUSH TO CENTER. (BOTH SIDES)

$\frac{1}{2}$ I.D. BLACK PIPE 12" LONG (2 REQ.)

$\frac{1}{2}$ I.D. BLACK PIPE 8" LONG

GRIND ENDS TO FIT.

ELEVATE CENTER 2"

$\frac{3}{4}$ I.D. RUBBER END CAPS (3 REQ.)

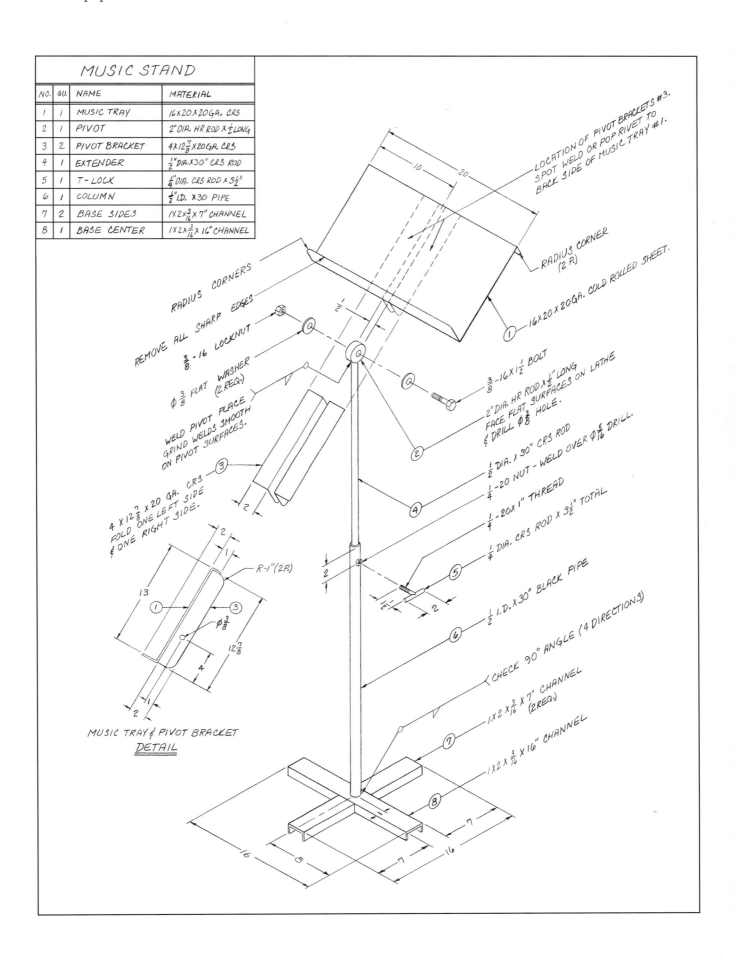

MUSIC STAND

NO.	QU.	NAME	MATERIAL
1	1	MUSIC TRAY	16X20X20GA. CRS
2	1	PIVOT	2" DIA. HR ROD X $\frac{1}{2}$ LONG
3	2	PIVOT BRACKET	4X12$\frac{7}{8}$X20GA. CRS
4	1	EXTENDER	$\frac{1}{2}$" DIA. X30" CRS ROD
5	1	T-LOCK	$\frac{1}{4}$" DIA. CRS ROD X 3$\frac{1}{2}$"
6	1	COLUMN	$\frac{1}{2}$" I.D. X30 PIPE
7	2	BASE SIDES	1X2X$\frac{3}{16}$X 7" CHANNEL
8	1	BASE CENTER	1X2X$\frac{3}{16}$X 16" CHANNEL

LOCATION OF PIVOT BRACKETS #3.
SPOT WELD OR POP RIVET TO
BACK SIDE OF MUSIC TRAY #1.

RADIUS CORNER
(2 P.)

16X20 X 20GA. COLD ROLLED SHEET.

RADIUS CORNERS

REMOVE ALL SHARP EDGES

$\frac{3}{8}$ - 16 LOCKNUT

$\phi \frac{3}{8}$ FLAT WASHER
(2 REQ.)

$\frac{3}{8}$ -16 X 1$\frac{1}{2}$ BOLT

2" DIA. HR ROD X $\frac{1}{2}$" LONG
FACE FLAT SURFACES ON LATHE
& DRILL $\phi \frac{3}{8}$ HOLE.

WELD PIVOT PLACE
GRIND WELDS SMOOTH
ON PIVOT SURFACES.

$\frac{1}{2}$ DIA. X 30" CRS ROD

$\frac{1}{4}$-20 NUT - WELD OVER $\phi \frac{5}{16}$ DRILL.

$\frac{1}{4}$ -20X 1" THREAD

$\frac{1}{4}$ DIA. CRS ROD X 3$\frac{1}{2}$" TOTAL

4 X 12$\frac{7}{8}$ X 20 GA. CRS
FOLD ONE LEFT SIDE
& ONE RIGHT SIDE.

R-1"(2 P.)

$\phi \frac{3}{8}$

MUSIC TRAY & PIVOT BRACKET
<u>DETAIL</u>

$\frac{1}{2}$ I.D. X 30" BLACK PIPE

CHECK 90° ANGLE (4 DIRECTIONS)

1X 2 X $\frac{3}{16}$ X 7" CHANNEL
(2 REQ.)

1X2 X $\frac{3}{16}$ X 16" CHANNEL

ELECTRIC PIANO STAND			
NO.	QU.	NAME	MATERIAL
1	2	FRAME SIDE	1×1×⅛ L IRON T.B.D.
2	2	FRAME END	1×1×⅛ L IRON T.B.D.
3	2	LEG	½ I.D. PIPE T.B.D.
4	2	LEG SUPPORT SIDE	⅜ DIA. CRS T.B.D
5	1	LEG SUPPORT BACK	⅜ DIA. CRS T.B.D.

FIT TOP FRAME TO BASE OF ELECTRIC PIANO.

$\mathbb{A}$ — LENGTH OF BASE

$\mathbb{B}$ — WIDTH OF BASE

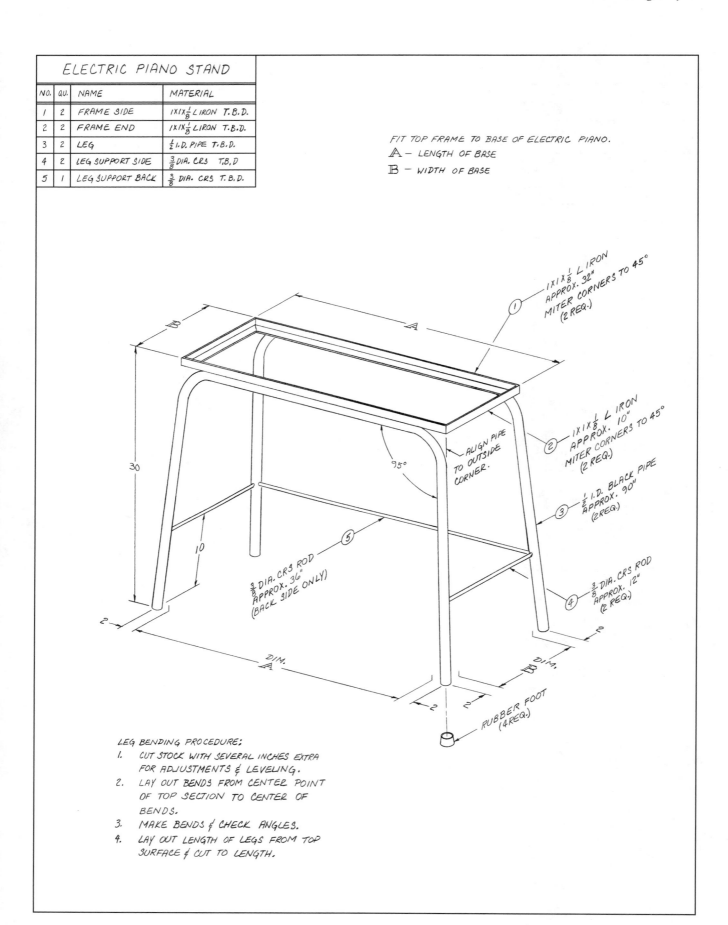

LEG BENDING PROCEDURE:

1. CUT STOCK WITH SEVERAL INCHES EXTRA
    FOR ADJUSTMENTS & LEVELING.
2. LAY OUT BENDS FROM CENTER POINT
    OF TOP SECTION TO CENTER OF
    BENDS.
3. MAKE BENDS & CHECK ANGLES.
4. LAY OUT LENGTH OF LEGS FROM TOP
    SURFACE & CUT TO LENGTH.

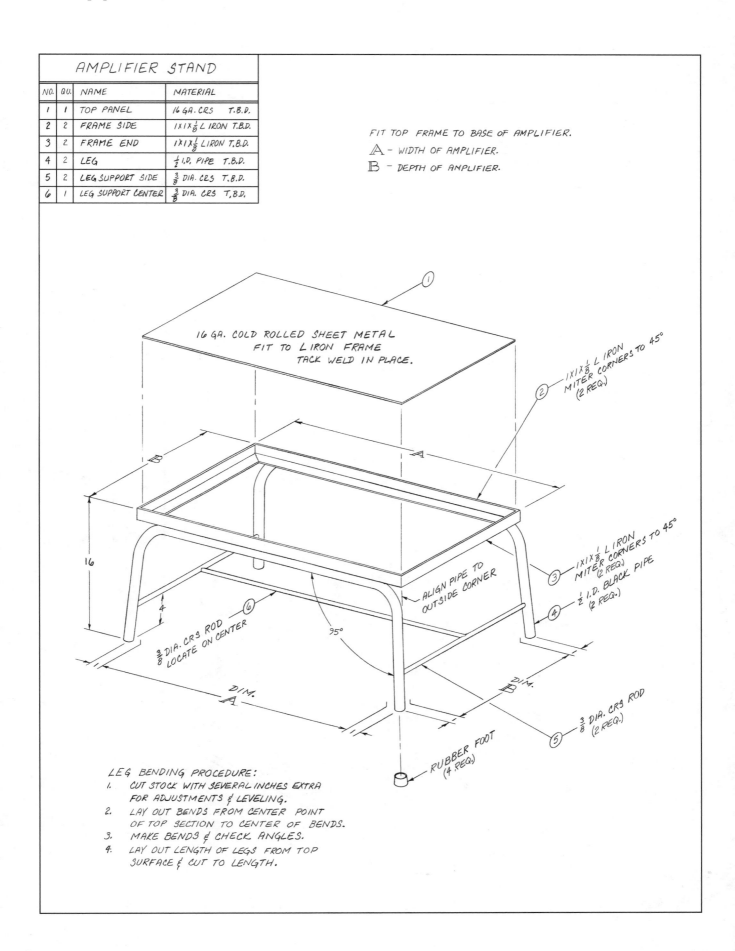

AMPLIFIER STAND			
NO.	QU.	NAME	MATERIAL
1	1	TOP PANEL	16 GA. CRS T.B.D.
2	2	FRAME SIDE	1X1X⅛ L IRON T.B.D.
3	2	FRAME END	1X1X⅛ L IRON T.B.D.
4	2	LEG	½ I.D. PIPE T.B.D.
5	2	LEG SUPPORT SIDE	⅜ DIA. CRS T.B.D.
6	1	LEG SUPPORT CENTER	⅜ DIA. CRS T.B.D.

FIT TOP FRAME TO BASE OF AMPLIFIER.

A - WIDTH OF AMPLIFIER.

B - DEPTH OF AMPLIFIER.

16 GA. COLD ROLLED SHEET METAL
FIT TO L IRON FRAME
TACK WELD IN PLACE.

1X1X⅛ L IRON
MITER CORNERS TO 45°
(2 REQ.)

1X1X⅛ L IRON
MITER CORNERS TO 45°
(2 REQ.)

½ I.D. BLACK PIPE
(2 REQ.)

⅜ DIA. CRS ROD
(2 REQ.)

⅜ DIA. CRS ROD
LOCATE ON CENTER

ALIGN PIPE TO
OUTSIDE CORNER

RUBBER FOOT
(4 REQ.)

95°

16

4

DIM.
A

DIM.
B

LEG BENDING PROCEDURE:

1. CUT STOCK WITH SEVERAL INCHES EXTRA
    FOR ADJUSTMENTS & LEVELING.
2. LAY OUT BENDS FROM CENTER POINT
    OF TOP SECTION TO CENTER OF BENDS.
3. MAKE BENDS & CHECK ANGLES.
4. LAY OUT LENGTH OF LEGS FROM TOP
    SURFACE & CUT TO LENGTH.

NO.	QU.	NAME	MATERIAL
1	1	STAND	4" I.D. X 7" PIPE
2	3	ADJUSTING SCREW	$\frac{3}{8}$ X 6" CRS ROD
3	1	BOTTOM	$\frac{1}{4}$ X 10 X 10 HR PLATE
4	1	CENTER SPIKE	$\emptyset \frac{5}{16}$ X 1" CRS ROD
5	1	BASE	$\frac{1}{2}$ X 20 X 20 PLYWOOD

CHRISTMAS TREE STAND

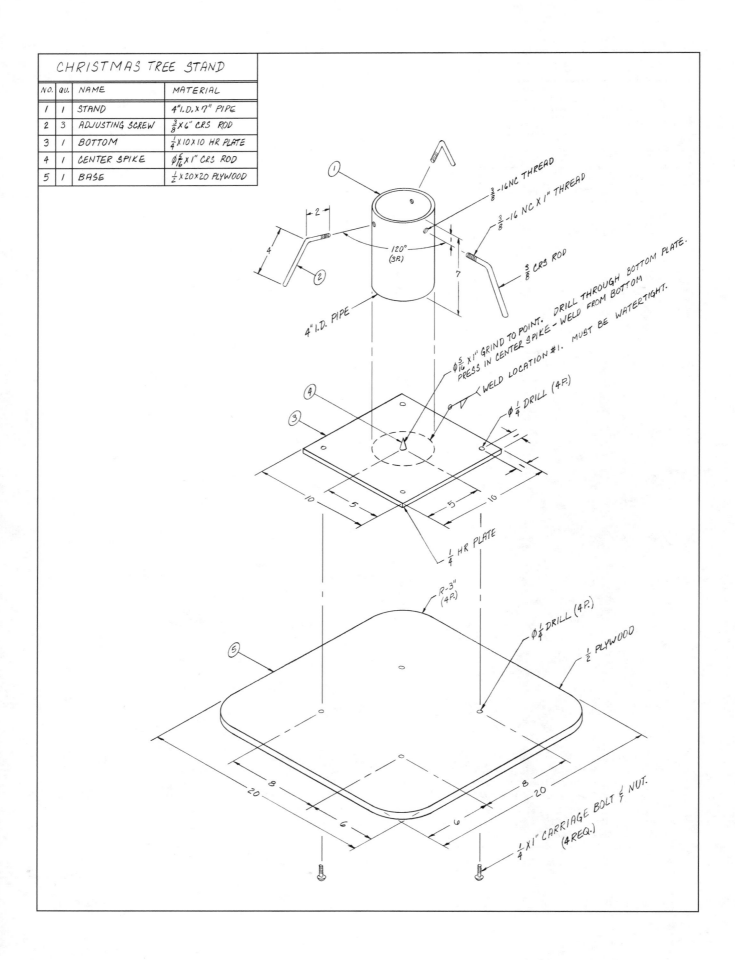

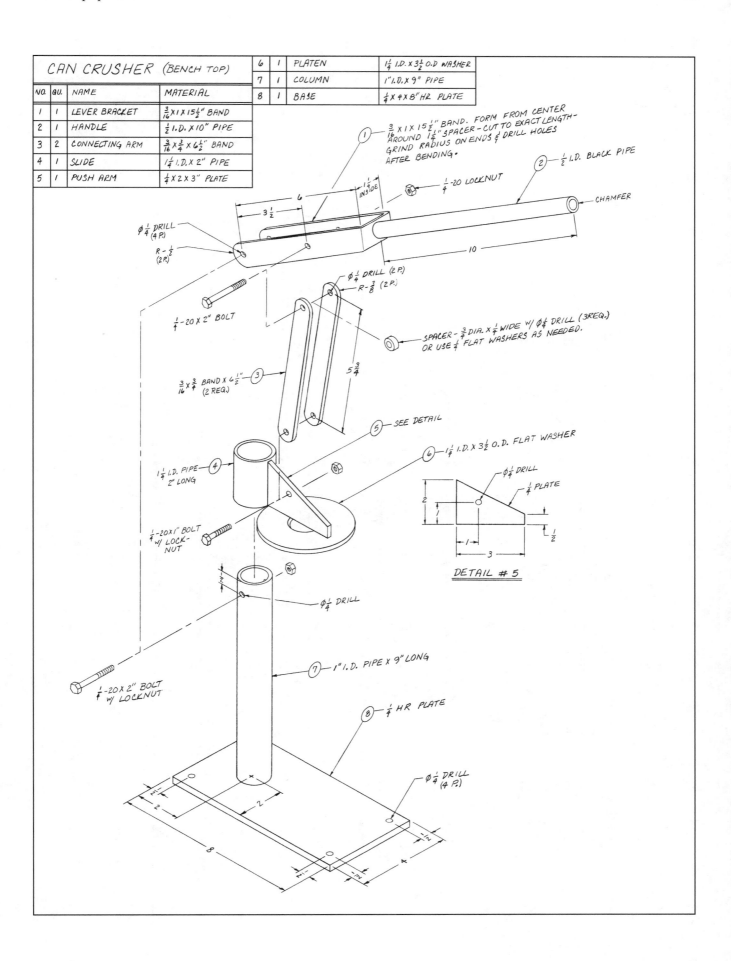

CAN CRUSHER (BENCH TOP)

NO.	QU.	NAME	MATERIAL
1	1	LEVER BRACKET	$\frac{3}{16}$ X 1 X 15$\frac{1}{2}$" BAND
2	1	HANDLE	$\frac{1}{2}$ I.D. X 10" PIPE
3	2	CONNECTING ARM	$\frac{3}{16}$ X $\frac{3}{4}$ X 6$\frac{1}{2}$" BAND
4	1	SLIDE	1$\frac{1}{4}$ I.D. X 2" PIPE
5	1	PUSH ARM	$\frac{1}{4}$ X 2 X 3" PLATE
6	1	PLATEN	1$\frac{1}{4}$ I.D. X 3$\frac{1}{2}$ O.D WASHER
7	1	COLUMN	1" I.D. X 9" PIPE
8	1	BASE	$\frac{1}{4}$ X 4 X 8" HR PLATE

DETAIL # 5

NO.	QU.	NAME	MATERIAL									
		BAKER'S RACK		4	2	FRONT SUPPORT	$\frac{3}{8}$ DIA. X 33" HR. ROD	10	2	SCROLL	$\frac{1}{4}$ DIA. X 28" CRS ROD
				5	2	LARGE SHELF BRKT.	SEE NOTE	11	2	SCROLL	$\frac{1}{4}$ DIA. X 19" CRS ROD
NO.	QU.	NAME	MATERIAL	6	1	SMALL SHELF BRKT.	SEE NOTE	12	2	SCROLL	$\frac{1}{4}$ DIA. X 34" CRS ROD
1	2	BACK LEG	$\frac{1}{2}$ I.D. X 60" PIPE	7	1	TOP BAR	$\frac{1}{2}$ I.D. X 39" PIPE	13	4	SCROLL	$\frac{1}{4}$ DIA. X 42" CRS ROD
2	2	FRONT LEG	$\frac{1}{2}$ I.D. X 32" PIPE	8	1	CENTER SUPPORT	$\frac{1}{4}$ X 1 X 54" FLAT	14	4	END CAP	1" DIA. X 2$\frac{1}{2}$ AL. ROD
3	2	BACK SUPPORT	$\frac{3}{8}$ DIA. X 61" HR. ROD	9	3	BACK BAR	$\frac{1}{4}$ DIA. X 36 CRS ROD	15	3	SHELVES	SEE NOTE

NOTE:
LENGTHS OF RODS FOR SCROLLS MAY
VARY DEPENDING ON SCROLLING DIE
BEING USED.

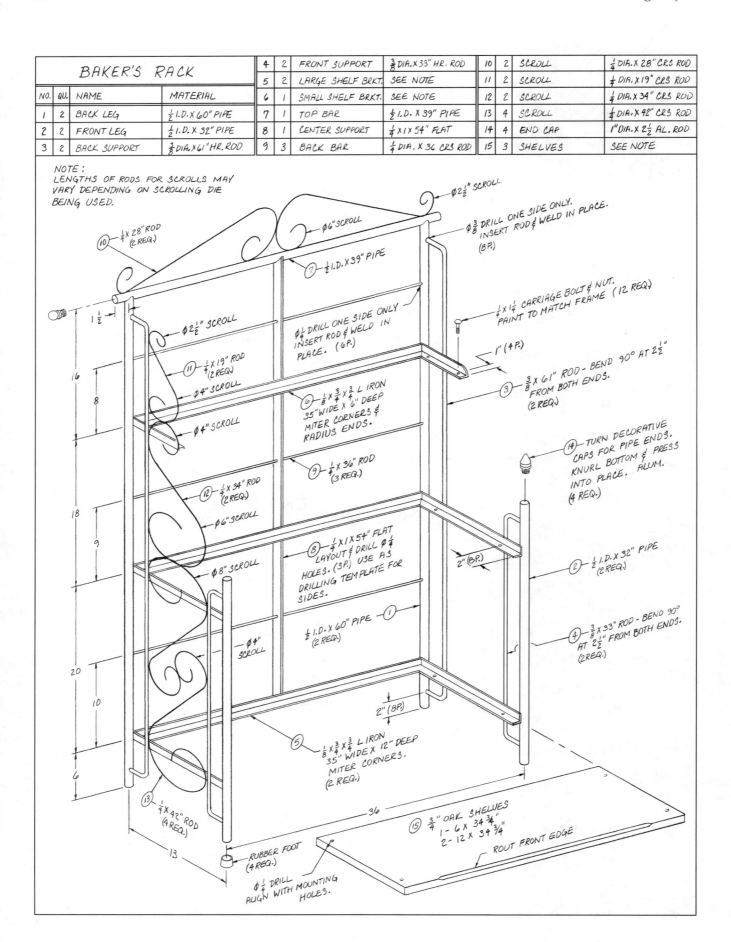

CORNER BAKER'S RACK

NO.	QU.	NAME	MATERIAL
1	1	CORNER FRAME	$\frac{3}{4} \times \frac{3}{4} \times 50$" HR. SQUARE
2	2	LEG	$\frac{3}{4} \times \frac{3}{4} \times 20$" HR. SQUARE
3	2	BOT. SHELF BRKT.	$\frac{1}{8} \times \frac{3}{4} \times \frac{3}{4} \times 18$" L IRON
4	2	MID. SHELF BRKT.	$\frac{1}{8} \times \frac{3}{4} \times \frac{3}{4} \times 15$" L IRON
5	2	TOP SHELF BRKT.	$\frac{1}{8} \times \frac{3}{4} \times \frac{3}{4} \times 12$" L IRON

6	2	SHELF SUPPORT	$\frac{1}{4}$ DIA. X $35\frac{1}{2}$" CRS ROD
7	2	SCROLL	$\frac{1}{4}$ DIA. X 15" CRS ROD
8	4	SCROLL	$\frac{1}{4}$ DIA. X 22" CRS ROD
9	4	SCROLL	$\frac{1}{4}$ DIA. X 38" CRS ROD
10	4	SCROLL	$\frac{1}{4}$ DIA. X 46" CRS ROD
11	1	TOP SHELF	SEE DETAIL
12	1	MIDDLE SHELF	SEE DETAIL
13	1	BOTTOM SHELF	SEE DETAIL

NOTE:

LENGTHS OF RODS FOR SCROLLS MAY VARY DEPENDING ON SCROLLING DIE BEING USED.

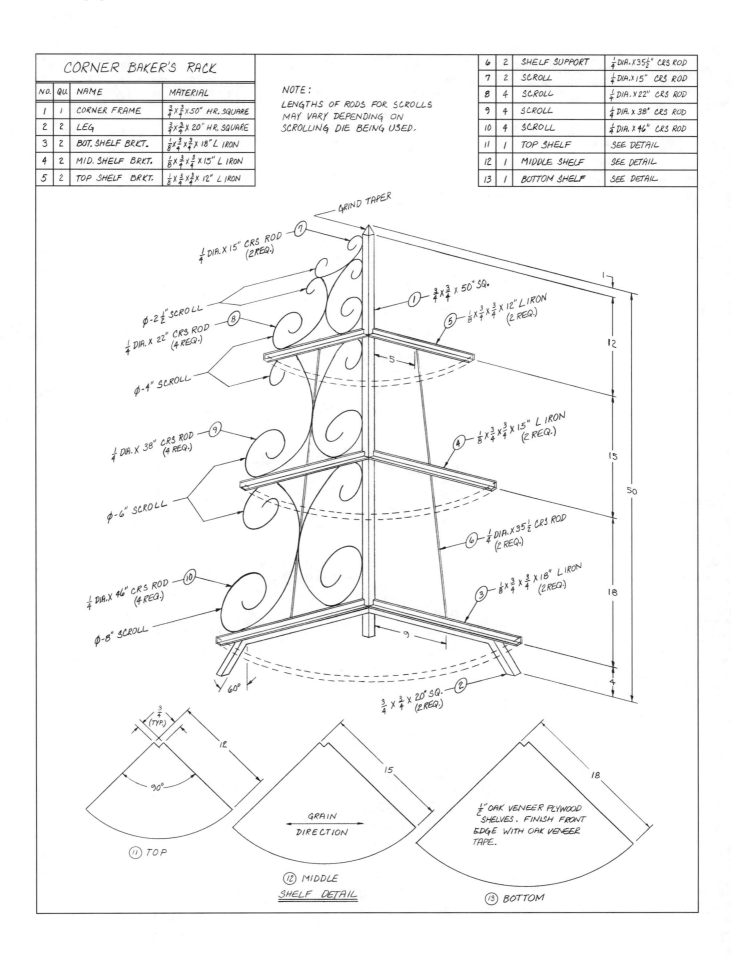

FOUR-SHELF PLANT STAND

NO.	QU.	NAME	MATERIAL
1	2	BACK FRAME	$\frac{1}{2} \times \frac{1}{2} \times 60"$ HR. SQ.
2	1	TOP FRAME	$\frac{1}{2} \times \frac{1}{2} \times 24"$ HR. SQ.
3	1	SHELF SUPPORT	$\frac{1}{8} \times \frac{1}{2} \times \frac{1}{2} \times 58"$ L IRON
4	1	SHELF SUPPORT	$\frac{1}{8} \times \frac{1}{2} \times \frac{1}{2} \times 63"$ L IRON
5	1	SHELF SUPPORT	$\frac{1}{8} \times \frac{1}{2} \times \frac{1}{2} \times 68"$ L IRON
6	1	SHELF SUPPORT	$\frac{1}{8} \times \frac{1}{2} \times \frac{1}{2} \times 73"$ L IRON
7	2	LEG	$\frac{1}{2} \times \frac{1}{2} \times 4"$ HR. SQ.
8	2	SCROLL	$\frac{1}{8} \times \frac{1}{2} \times 22"$ BAND
9	2	SCROLL	$\frac{1}{8} \times \frac{1}{2} \times 26"$ BAND
10	2	SCROLL	$\frac{1}{8} \times \frac{1}{2} \times 30"$ BAND
11	2	SCROLL	$\frac{1}{8} \times \frac{1}{2} \times 34"$ BAND
12	2	SCROLL	$\frac{1}{8} \times \frac{1}{2} \times 14"$ BAND
13	2	SCROLL	$\frac{1}{8} \times \frac{1}{2} \times 29"$ BAND
14	4	SHELVES	SEE NOTE

NOTES:
1. LENGTH OF STOCK FOR SCROLLS MAY VARY DEPENDING ON SCROLLING DIE BEING USED.
2. ALL SCROLLS SHOWN ARE Ø-2½" UNLESS OTHERWISE NOTED.

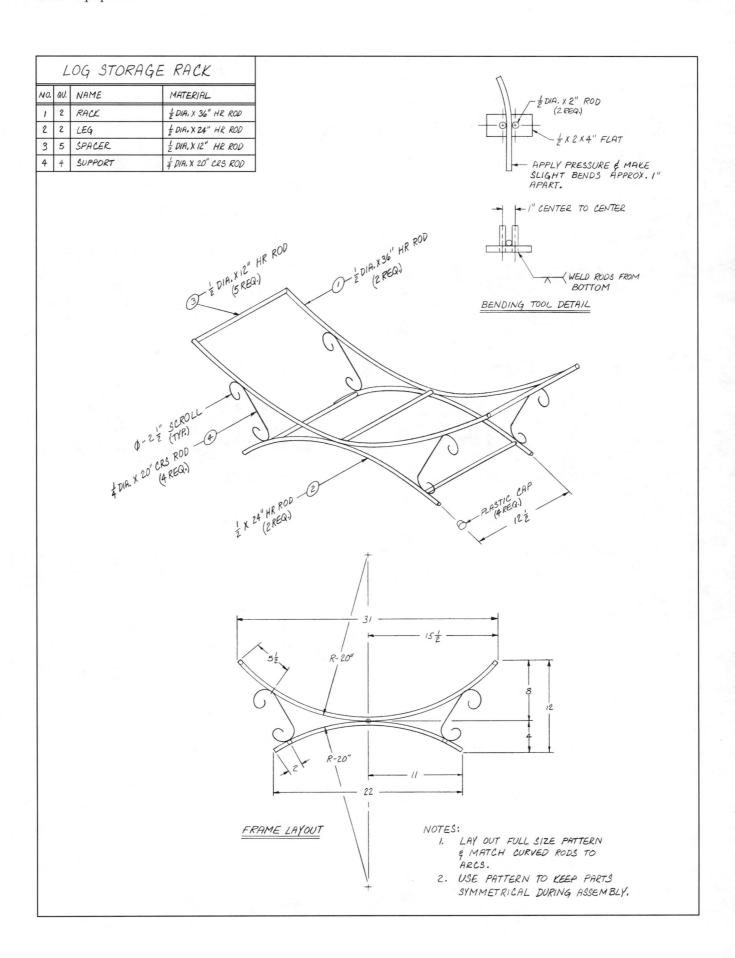

LOG STORAGE RACK

NO.	QU.	NAME	MATERIAL
1	2	RACK	½ DIA. X 36" HR ROD
2	2	LEG	½ DIA. X 24" HR ROD
3	5	SPACER	½ DIA. X 12" HR ROD
4	4	SUPPORT	¼ DIA. X 20" CRS ROD

③ ½ DIA. X 12" HR ROD (5 REQ.)

① ½ DIA. X 36" HR ROD (2 REQ.)

Ø - 2 ½" SCROLL (TYP.)

¼ DIA. X 20" CRS ROD (4 REQ.)

④

½ X 24" HR ROD (2 REQ.) — ②

PLASTIC CAP (4 REQ.)

12 ½

½ DIA. X 2" ROD (2 REQ.)

½ X 2 X 4" FLAT

APPLY PRESSURE & MAKE SLIGHT BENDS APPROX. 1" APART.

1" CENTER TO CENTER

WELD RODS FROM BOTTOM

BENDING TOOL DETAIL

FRAME LAYOUT

31

15 ½

5 ½

R-20"

8

12

4

2

R-20"

11

22

NOTES:
1. LAY OUT FULL SIZE PATTERN & MATCH CURVED RODS TO ARCS.
2. USE PATTERN TO KEEP PARTS SYMMETRICAL DURING ASSEMBLY.

Yard Equipment

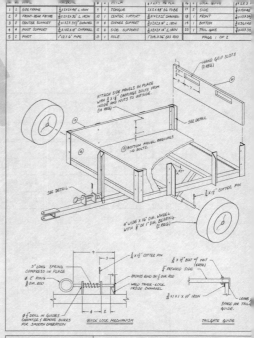

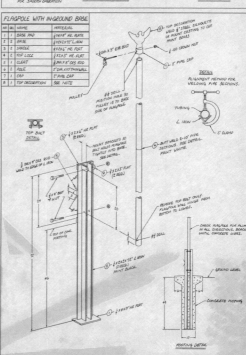

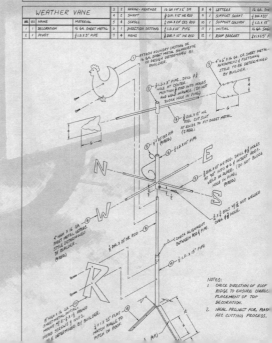

HAND-PUSH LAWN WAGON

NO.	QU.	NAME	MATERIAL
1	1	HANDLE	$\frac{1}{2}$ I.D x 93" PIPE
2	2	SIDE-TOP RAIL	$\frac{3}{16}$ x 1 x 40" HR FLAT
3	2	END-TOP RAIL	$\frac{3}{16}$ x 1 x 22" HR FLAT
4	2	FRONT CORNER	1x1x $\frac{3}{16}$ x 13" L IRON
5	2	REAR CORNER	1x1x $\frac{3}{16}$ x 25" L IRON
6	2	END-BASE FRAME	1x1x $\frac{3}{16}$ x 22" L IRON
7	2	SIDE-BASE FRAME	1x1x $\frac{3}{16}$ x 40" L IRON
8	2	CROSS MEMBER	1x1x $\frac{3}{16}$ x 32" L IRON
9	2	WHEEL SUPPORT	$\frac{1}{4}$ x 1 x 24" HR FLAT
10	2	OUTER FORK	$\frac{1}{4}$ x 1 x 2" HR FLAT
11	2	INNER FORK	$\frac{1}{4}$ x 1 x 3" HR FLAT
12	2	LEG	$\frac{1}{4}$ x 1 x 19$\frac{1}{2}$" HR FLAT
13	1	BOTTOM	$\frac{1}{2}$ x 23$\frac{1}{2}$ x 41$\frac{1}{2}$" PLYWOOD
14	2	END	$\frac{1}{2}$ x 12$\frac{1}{2}$ x 23$\frac{1}{2}$" PLYWOOD
15	2	SIDE	$\frac{1}{2}$ x 12$\frac{1}{2}$ x 40$\frac{1}{2}$" PLYWOOD

NOTES:

1. SCREW PLYWOOD SIDES TO FRAME WITH 6 - $\frac{1}{4}$ x 1 CARRIAGE BOLTS FROM INSIDE & NUTS TO OUTSIDE. (TO BE LOCATED) BOTTOM & ENDS ARE SANDWICHED IN PLACE BY SIDES.
2. PAINT FRAME & PLYWOOD SEPARATELY BEFORE FINAL ASSEMBLY.
3. USE TREATED PLYWOOD FOR BOTTOM & SIDES.

24 INSIDE TO INSIDE

RADIUS END

SEE DETAIL

20" BICYCLE WHEEL

$\frac{1}{4}$ x 1 FLAT

MILL SLOT 1" DEEP x $\frac{3}{8}$ WIDE

DETAIL #10 (2 REQ.)

DETAIL #11 (2 REQ.)

TOP RAILS BUTT TO L IRON FLANGE. (FRONT, BACK & SIDES.)

20" DIA. MAX.

E-Z TILT LAWN CART				6	1	AXLE BRACKET	1" I.D. X 10" PIPE	14	2	TAIL GATE GUIDE	$\frac{3}{16}$ X 1 X 1 X 10" L IRON
				7	2	GUSSET	$\frac{1}{4}$ X 3 X 3" HR PLATE	15	1	TILT LOCK	SEE ASSEMBLY
NO.	QU.	NAME	MATERIAL	8	2	HITCH	$\frac{1}{4}$ X 2 X 7" HR FLAT	16	2	LOCK GUIDE	$\frac{1}{4}$ X 2 X 3" HR FLAT
1	2	SIDE FRAME	$\frac{3}{16}$ X 2 X 2 X 48" L IRON	9	1	TONGUE	2 X 2 X 48" SQ. TUBE	17	2	SIDE	$\frac{3}{4}$ X 10 X 48" PLYWOOD
2	2	FRONT- REAR FRAME	$\frac{3}{16}$ X 2 X 2 X 36" L IRON	10	1	CENTER SUPPORT	$\frac{3}{16}$ X 1 X 2 X 22" CHANNEL	18	1	FRONT	$\frac{3}{4}$ X 10 X 34$\frac{1}{2}$" PLYWOOD
3	2	CENTER SUPPORT	$\frac{3}{16}$ X 1 X 2 X 35$\frac{1}{2}$" CHANNEL	11	4	CORNER SUPPORT	$\frac{3}{16}$ X 2 X 2 X 14" L IRON	19	1	BOTTOM	$\frac{3}{4}$ X 36 X 48" PLYWOOD
4	4	PIVOT SUPPORT	$\frac{3}{16}$ X 1 X 2 X 14" CHANNEL	12	4	SIDE SUPPORTS	$\frac{3}{16}$ X 2 X 2 X 14" L IRON	20	1	TAIL GATE	$\frac{3}{4}$ X 10 X 34$\frac{1}{4}$" PLYWOOD
5	2	PIVOT	1" I.D. X 6" PIPE	13	1	AXLE	1" DIA. X 36" CRS ROD			PAGE 1 OF 2	

HAND GRIP SLOTS
(2 REQ.)

ATTACH SIDE PANELS IN PLACE
WITH $\frac{3}{16}$ X 1$\frac{1}{4}$" CARRIAGE BOLTS FROM
INSIDE AND NUTS TO OUTSIDE.
(18 REQ.)

SEE DETAIL

BOTTOM PANEL REQUIRES
NO BOLTS.

45°

SEE DETAIL

$\frac{3}{16}$ X 1$\frac{1}{2}$" COTTER PIN

4" WIDE X 16" DIA. WHEEL
WITH $\frac{3}{4}$" OR 1" DIA. BEARING.
(2 REQ.)

QUICK LOCK MECHANISM

5" LONG SPRING
COMPRESS IN PLACE

Ø 2" RING
$\frac{3}{8}$ DIA. ROD

$\frac{3}{16}$ X 1$\frac{1}{2}$" COTTER PIN

RADIUS END ON $\frac{1}{2}$ DIA. ROD

WELD TAPER-LOCK
INSIDE CHANNEL

Ø $\frac{1}{2}$" DRILL IN GUIDES
CHAMFER & REMOVE BURRS
FOR SMOOTH OPERATION

TAILGATE GUIDE

$\frac{5}{16}$ X 1$\frac{1}{2}$" BOLT W/ NUT
(4 REQ.)

$\frac{3}{4}$ PLYWOOD SIDE

$\frac{3}{16}$ X 1 X 1 X 10" IRON

LEAVE $\frac{7}{8}$"
SPACE FOR TAILGATE
GUIDE.

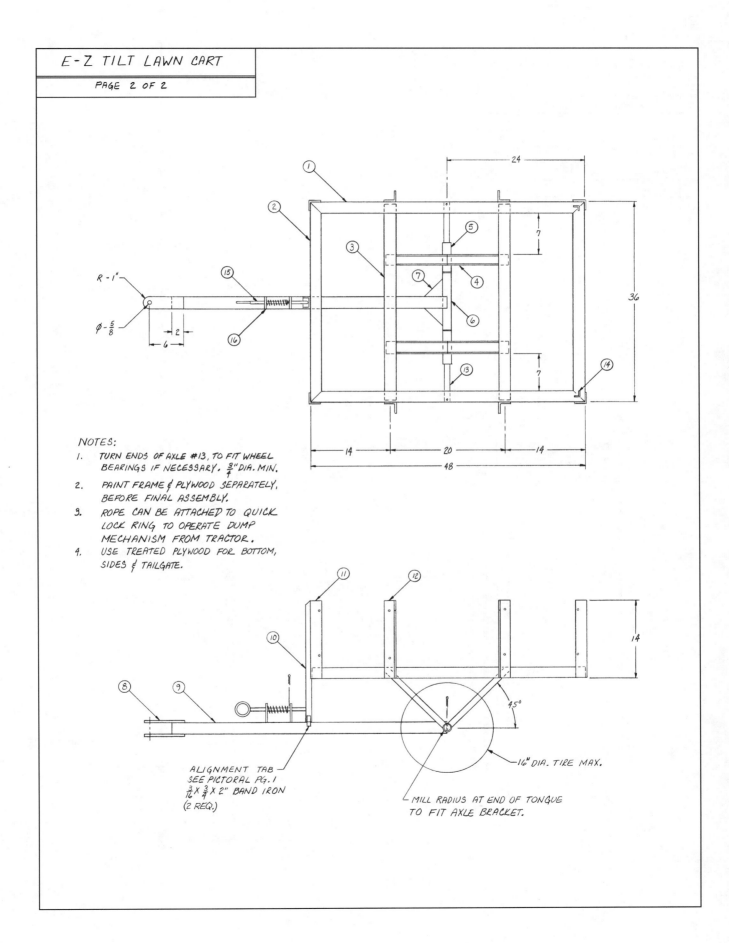

E-Z TILT LAWN CART

PAGE 2 OF 2

NOTES:
1. TURN ENDS OF AXLE #13, TO FIT WHEEL BEARINGS IF NECESSARY. $\frac{3}{4}$" DIA. MIN.
2. PAINT FRAME & PLYWOOD SEPARATELY, BEFORE FINAL ASSEMBLY.
3. ROPE CAN BE ATTACHED TO QUICK LOCK RING TO OPERATE DUMP MECHANISM FROM TRACTOR.
4. USE TREATED PLYWOOD FOR BOTTOM, SIDES & TAILGATE.

R - 1"
$\phi - \frac{5}{8}$

ALIGNMENT TAB
SEE PICTORAL PG.1
$\frac{3}{16}$ X $\frac{3}{4}$ X 2" BAND IRON
(2 REQ.)

16" DIA. TIRE MAX.

MILL RADIUS AT END OF TONGUE TO FIT AXLE BRACKET.

45°

FLAGPOLE WITH IN-GROUND BASE

NO.	QU.	NAME	MATERIAL
1	1	BASE PAD	$\frac{1}{4}$X4X8" HR. PLATE
2	2	BASE	$\frac{1}{4}$X2X2X72" L IRON
3	2	SPACER	$\frac{1}{4}$X2X6" HR. FLAT
4	2	TOP LOCK	$\frac{1}{4}$X2X3" HR. FLAT
5	1	CLEAT	$\frac{3}{8}$DIA.X8" CRS ROD
6	2	POLE	2" DIA.X10' THINWALL
7	1	CAP	2" PIPE CAP
8	1	TOP DECORATION	SEE NOTE

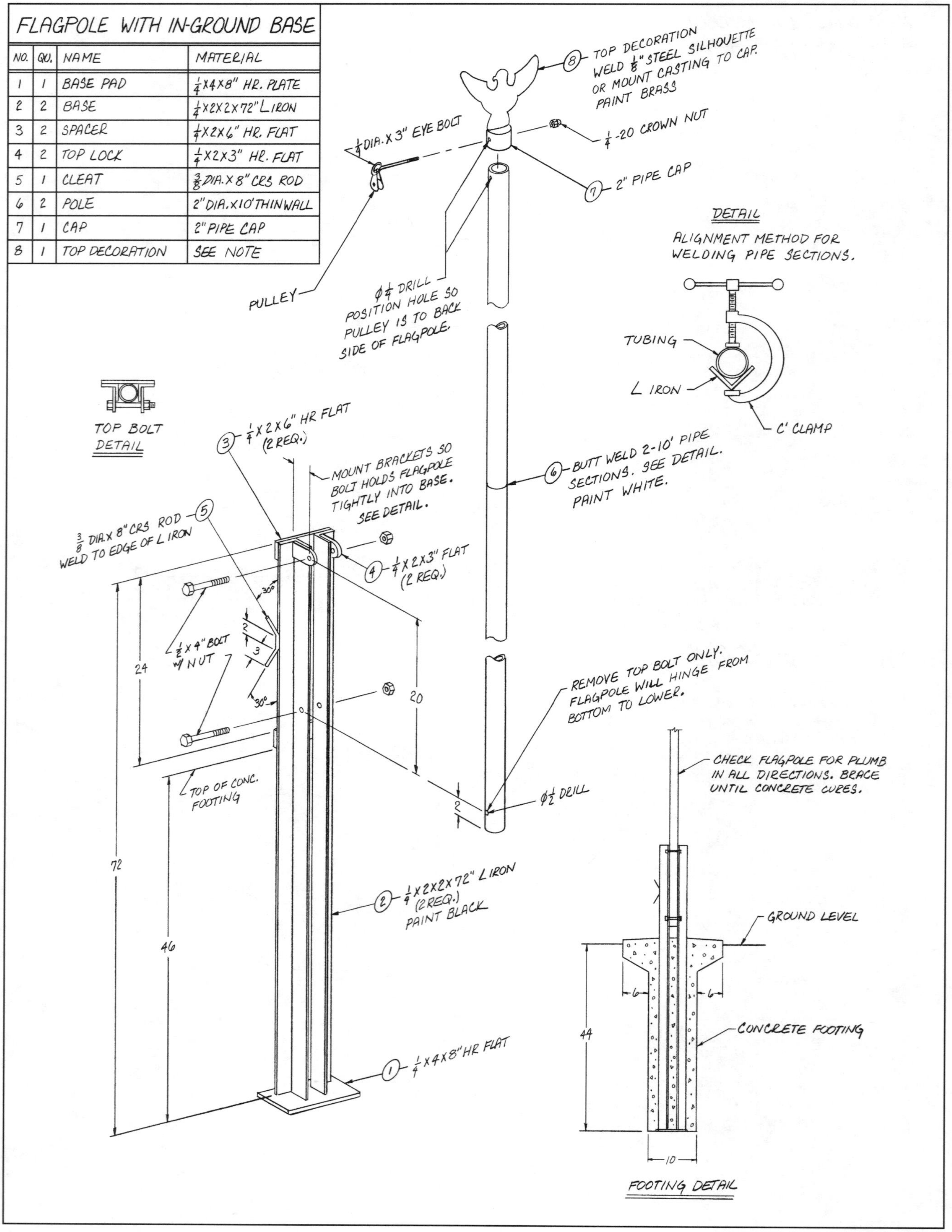

(8) TOP DECORATION WELD $\frac{1}{8}$" STEEL SILHOUETTE OR MOUNT CASTING TO CAP. PAINT BRASS
$\frac{1}{4}$ DIA. X 3" EYE BOLT
$\frac{1}{4}$-20 CROWN NUT
(7) 2" PIPE CAP
PULLEY
$\phi\frac{1}{4}$ DRILL POSITION HOLE SO PULLEY IS TO BACK SIDE OF FLAGPOLE.
DETAIL
ALIGNMENT METHOD FOR WELDING PIPE SECTIONS.
TUBING
L IRON
C' CLAMP
TOP BOLT DETAIL
(3) $\frac{1}{4}$X2X6" HR FLAT (2 REQ.)
MOUNT BRACKETS SO BOLT HOLDS FLAGPOLE TIGHTLY INTO BASE. SEE DETAIL.
(6) BUTT WELD 2-10' PIPE SECTIONS. SEE DETAIL. PAINT WHITE.
$\frac{3}{8}$ DIA.X 8" CRS ROD (5) WELD TO EDGE OF L IRON
(4) $\frac{1}{4}$X2X3" FLAT (2 REQ.)
30°
2
3
$\frac{1}{2}$X4" BOLT W/ NUT
24
20
30°
REMOVE TOP BOLT ONLY. FLAGPOLE WILL HINGE FROM BOTTOM TO LOWER.
TOP OF CONC. FOOTING
2
$\phi\frac{1}{2}$ DRILL
CHECK FLAGPOLE FOR PLUMB IN ALL DIRECTIONS. BRACE UNTIL CONCRETE CURES.
72
(2) $\frac{1}{4}$X2X2X72" L IRON (2 REQ.) PAINT BLACK
46
GROUND LEVEL
6
6
CONCRETE FOOTING
44
(1) $\frac{1}{4}$X4X8" HR FLAT
10
FOOTING DETAIL

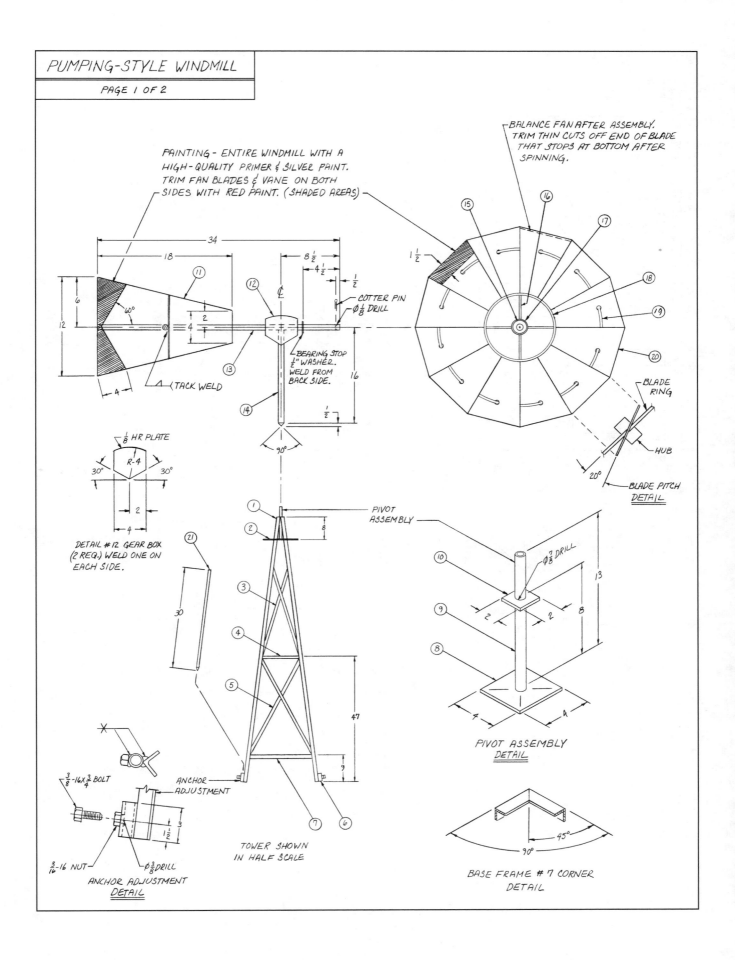

PUMPING-STYLE WINDMILL

PAGE 1 OF 2

PAINTING - ENTIRE WINDMILL WITH A HIGH-QUALITY PRIMER & SILVER PAINT. TRIM FAN BLADES & VANE ON BOTH SIDES WITH RED PAINT. (SHADED AREAS)

BALANCE FAN AFTER ASSEMBLY. TRIM THIN CUTS OFF END OF BLADE THAT STOPS AT BOTTOM AFTER SPINNING.

COTTER PIN
Ø ⅛ DRILL

BEARING STOP ½" WASHER. WELD FROM BACK SIDE.

TACK WELD

⅛ HR PLATE

DETAIL #12 GEAR BOX (2 REQ.) WELD ONE ON EACH SIDE.

BLADE RING

HUB

BLADE PITCH
DETAIL

PIVOT ASSEMBLY

Ø ⅞ DRILL

PIVOT ASSEMBLY
DETAIL

ANCHOR ADJUSTMENT

⅜-16 X ¾ BOLT

⅜-16 NUT

Ø ⅜ DRILL

ANCHOR ADJUSTMENT
DETAIL

TOWER SHOWN IN HALF SCALE

BASE FRAME #7 CORNER DETAIL

PUMPING-STYLE WINDMILL

NO.	QU.	NAME	MATERIAL
1	4	LEG	$\frac{1}{8}$"X1"X1"X 96" L IRON
2	1	FAN GUARD	12"X12"X18 GA. CRS
3	8	UPPER CROSS MEMBER	$\frac{1}{8}$X$\frac{3}{4}$ X 36" HR BAND
4	4	CENTER BRACE	$\frac{1}{8}$ X $\frac{3}{4}$ X 13$\frac{1}{2}$" HR BAND
5	8	LOWER CROSS MEMBER	$\frac{1}{8}$ X$\frac{3}{4}$ X 41" HR BAND
6	4	ANCHOR LOCK	SEE DETAIL
7	4	BASE FRAME	$\frac{1}{8}$"X1"X1"X 24" L IRON
8	1	PIVOT BASE	$\frac{1}{4}$"X4"X4" HR PLATE
9	1	PIVOT SLEEVE	$\frac{1}{2}$" I.D. BLACK PIPE
10	1	TOP SUPPORT	$\frac{1}{4}$ X 2"X2" HR PLATE
11	1	VANE	12"X18"X18 GA. CRS
12	2	GEAR BOX	$\frac{1}{8}$" HR PLATE
13	1	VANE-FAN AXLE	$\frac{1}{2}$ DIA. X34" CRS ROD
14	1	PIVOT	$\frac{1}{2}$ DIA. X 16" CRS ROD
15	2	BEARING (RADIAL)	SEE NOTE #2
16	4	SPOKE	$\frac{3}{16}$ X $\frac{3}{4}$ X 3$\frac{1}{2}$ HR BAND
17	1	HUB	1$\frac{1}{4}$ I.D. X 3$\frac{1}{2}$" PIPE
18	1	INNER RING	$\frac{3}{16}$ X $\frac{3}{4}$ X 26$\frac{5}{8}$"HR BAND
19	1	BLADE RING	$\frac{1}{4}$ DIA. X 58$\frac{1}{8}$" CRS ROD
20	12	FAN BLADE	SEE DETAIL 18 GA. CRS
21	4	ANCHOR STAKE	$\frac{1}{2}$ DIA. X 30" HR ROD

PAGE 2 OF 2

NOTES:
1. FOR ACCURATE BLADE PLACEMENT, LAY OUT FULL SIZE DIAGRAM OF FAN ASSEMBLY.
2. BALL BEARING #15 IS A RADIAL BEARING WITH A SHOULDER ON ONE SIDE. $\frac{1}{2}$ I.D. BORE & 1$\frac{3}{8}$ O.D. RACE. (2 REQ.)
3. NOS. 1 & 7 ADD TO MAKE EVEN 10' LENGTHS.
4. ANCHORING (PART #21) IS VERY IMPORTANT. SYSTEM ALSO WORKS AS A LEVELING ADJUSTMENT. CHECK FOR UNDERGROUND UTILITIES BEFORE DRIVING STAKES.
5. NOS. 18 & 19 CAN BE FORMED AROUND PAINT CANS OR SMALL BARRELS - CHECK ROUNDNESS AFTER WELDING INTO RING.
6. FAN DIAMETER IS 24" ACROSS FLATS.
7. NOS. 3-4-5 & 7 WELD TO INSIDE OF ANGLE-IRON LEGS. FOR BEST APPEARANCE KEEP ALL WELDS TO INSIDE OF STRUCTURE.

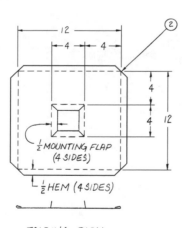

FOLDING PLAN
FAN GUARD #2
DETAIL

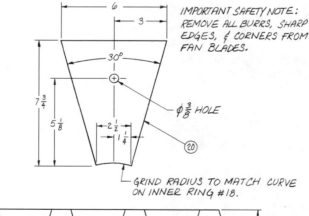

IMPORTANT SAFETY NOTE:
REMOVE ALL BURRS, SHARP EDGES, & CORNERS FROM FAN BLADES.

$\phi \frac{3}{8}$ HOLE

GRIND RADIUS TO MATCH CURVE ON INNER RING #18.

BLADE LAYOUT REVERSES FOR ECONOMICAL USE OF MAT'L.

FAN BLADE #20 (12 REQ.)
DETAIL

NO.	QU.	NAME	MATERIAL								
		WEATHER VANE		3	2	ARROW – FEATHER	16 GA X 4" X 6" SM	8	4	LETTERS	16 GA. SHEET METAL
				4	2	SHAFT	$\frac{3}{8}$ DIA. X 12" HR ROD	9	1	SUPPORT SHAFT	$\frac{1}{2}$ DIA. X 20" HR ROD
NO.	QU.	NAME	MATERIAL	5	4	SCROLL	$\frac{1}{4}$ DIA. X 20" CRS ROD	10	1	SUPPORT COLUMN	$\frac{1}{2}$ I.D. X 15" PIPE
1	1	DECORATION	16 GA. SHEET METAL	6	1	DIRECTION SETTING	$\frac{1}{2}$ I.D. X 10" PIPE	11	1	INITIAL	16 GA. SHEET METAL
2	1	PIVOT	$\frac{1}{2}$ I.D. X 3" PIPE	7	4	ARMS	$\frac{3}{8}$ DIA. X 10" HR ROD	12	1	ROOF BRACKET	$\frac{1}{4}$ X 1 X 25" FLAT

1 — ATTACH FOUNDRY CASTING OR 16 GA. SHEET METAL SILHOUETTE OF DESIGN DETERMINED BY BUILDER.

3 — 4" X 6" X 16 GA. CR SHEET METAL. ARROWHEAD & FLETCHING STYLE TO BE DETERMINED BY BUILDER.

2 — $\frac{1}{2}$ I.D. X 3" PIPE. DRILL $\phi\frac{3}{8}$ HOLE AT CENTER. POSITION $\frac{3}{8}$ ROD INTO HOLES AND WELD IN PLACE. (DO NOT BLOCK HOLE IN PIPE.)

4 — $\frac{3}{8}$ DIA. X 12" HR ROD. CUT SLOT AT ENDS TO FIT SHEET METAL (2 REQ.)

5 — $\frac{1}{4}$" X 20" CRS ROD (4 REQ.)

6 — $\frac{1}{2}$ I.D. X 10" PIPE

7 — $\frac{3}{8}$ DIA. X 10" HR ROD. DRILL $\phi\frac{3}{8}$ HOLES AT 90° INTO #6 & INSERT RODS. WELD IN PLACE. (DO NOT BLOCK HOLE IN PIPE.) (4 REQ.)

$\frac{5}{16}$ X $\frac{3}{4}$ BOLT W/ $\frac{5}{16}$ NUT WELDED OVER $\phi\frac{3}{8}$ HOLE.

8 — 4" HIGH X 16 GA. SHEET METAL LETTERS. STYLE DETERMINED BY BUILDER. (4 REQ.)

9 — $\frac{1}{2}$ DIA. X 20" HR ROD

CHECK ALIGNMENT BETWEEN ROD & PIPE.

10 — $\frac{1}{2}$ I.D. X 15" PIPE

11 — 8" HIGH X 16 GA. SHEET METAL INITIAL. MOUNT W/ 2 - $\frac{1}{4}$ X 1$\frac{1}{2}$ ROUND HEAD SCREWS & NUTS. STYLE DETERMINED BY BUILDER.

12 — $\frac{1}{4}$ X 1 X 25" FLAT. MATCH ANGLE TO PITCH OF ROOF.

$\phi\frac{5}{16}$ (4 P.)

NOTES:

1. CHECK DIRECTION OF ROOF RIDGE TO ENSURE CORRECT PLACEMENT OF TOP DECORATION.

2. IDEAL PROJECT FOR PLASMA ARC CUTTING PROCESS.

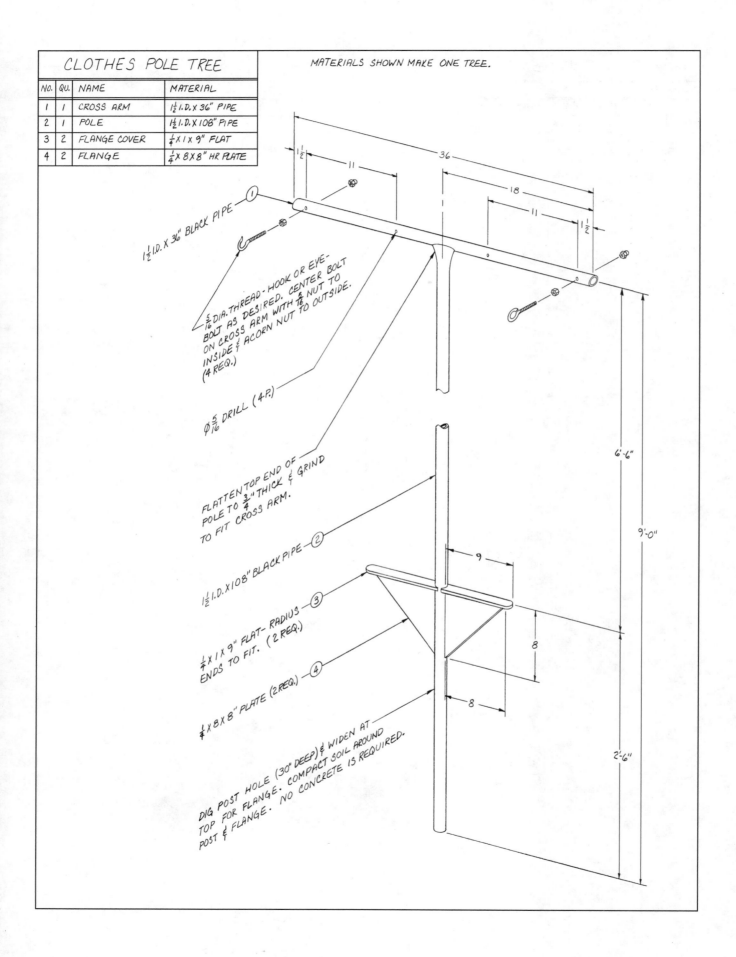

NO.	QU.	NAME	MATERIAL
1	1	CROSS ARM	$1\frac{1}{2}$ I.D. X 36" PIPE
2	1	POLE	$1\frac{1}{2}$ I.D. X 108" PIPE
3	2	FLANGE COVER	$\frac{1}{4}$ X 1 x 9" FLAT
4	2	FLANGE	$\frac{1}{4}$ X 8 X 8" HR PLATE

CLOTHES POLE TREE

MATERIALS SHOWN MAKE ONE TREE.

$1\frac{1}{2}$ I.D. X 36" BLACK PIPE

$\frac{5}{16}$ DIA. THREAD - HOOK OR EYE-BOLT AS DESIRED. CENTER BOLT ON CROSS ARM WITH $\frac{5}{16}$ NUT TO INSIDE & ACORN NUT TO OUTSIDE. (4 REQ.)

$\emptyset\frac{5}{16}$ DRILL (4 P.)

FLATTEN TOP END OF POLE TO $\frac{3}{4}$" THICK & GRIND TO FIT CROSS ARM.

$1\frac{1}{2}$ I.D. X 108" BLACK PIPE

$\frac{1}{4}$ X 1 X 9" FLAT - RADIUS ENDS TO FIT. (2 REQ.)

$\frac{1}{4}$ X 8 X 8" PLATE (2 REQ.)

DIG POST HOLE (30" DEEP) & WIDEN AT TOP FOR FLANGE. COMPACT SOIL AROUND POST & FLANGE. NO CONCRETE IS REQUIRED.